T|R|

ISLANDS
=IN=
THE BUSH

former colonial nations for basic information and data on their own country. Moreover, the prospect of repossessing major scientific collections would greatly encourage the growth of scientific institutions in the Third World. There is, of course, considerable variation in the degree of development of countries of the African continent, but I do feel strongly that Western scientists can do a great deal more to foster the growth of scientific research in the areas where they work to collect their raw data.

Malcolm Coe is a natural teacher and his ability to show enthusiasm and to engender it in others is a marvellous asset. Driving through the Kora area could be hazardous at the best of times with the narrow tracks, wash-outs and elephant-damaged trees which lie across the road. But to be driven as a visitor to the area with Malcolm at the wheel was an experience in itself. He spent so much time pointing out things of interest along the way that it was a miracle that he avoided colliding with the objects he was not intently examining. I particularly remember brushing past a large cow elephant which was on the edge of the track while Malcolm was pointing out the little mounds of earth in the road itself that had been made by the burrowing naked mole-rat. I think we would have gone under the elephant had it been standing across the road because Malcolm never saw it at all!

Teaching and passing on the know-how of fieldwork is of special importance on an expedition such as the Kora Research Project. Many young people in a country such as Kenya have had no opportunity to learn about how life is approached in the bush; even though many have had a rural upbringing, their contact with wild animals and the unexpected has been no greater than that of a city dweller. This background is often overlooked and many a young person has found himself or herself being expected to 'show the way' simply by virtue of being African in Africa. There were a number of Kenyans from my staff who spoke glowingly of Malcolm's personal effort to introduce them to the nyika and its animal inhabitants.

Amongst the hazards of Kora that the expedition faced, the lions were of greatest concern. With few exceptions these lions were animals that had once been in captivity but which George Adamson and his brother Terence have put back into the wild. The Adamsons had taught the lions to fend for themselves to a large extent but our concern was based on the fact that there was not much in the Kora area for them to hunt. Our party was very apprehensive that these hungry animals might prove less than friendly. Malcolm's story includes several anecdotes about these remarkable big cats and I won't spoil the book by divulging the details here, but I will say that, for me, their presence was a constant worry. The other animals that concerned me were the crocodiles, because the Tana River has many and they are well known for their habit of eating mammals. River crocodiles are notoriously dangerous and I was especially anxious for those of our team who were to spend time in the river sampling the aquatic fauna. Once many years ago I was attacked by a large river crocodile and I can recall to this day my horror as the huge reptile snapped at the small boat. The river crocodiles of Africa are renowned and I think we can be thankful that the Kora project was completed without incident.

In conclusion, I would like to turn to the whole issue of whether wild game can co-exist with human activities such as pastoralism. In Kora, there is very heavy pressure on the Reserve from herds of sheep, goats, cattle and camels which are in theory excluded from the area. The nomadic pastoralists build up huge herds of stock which are seldom managed on the basis of a fixed herd size related to the range available, and which today are larger than they would have been in the past because the animals benefit from veterinary care. These herds are simply destroying the vegetation and for them the pasture in the game reserves and national parks is the only possible short-term solution to their grazing requirements. Sadly, although the habitat destruction in the parks and reserves will eventually lead to the realization that traditional patterns of pastoralism don't work, by this time many game areas will have been so damaged that they will be lost forever.

It will require considerable political courage on the part of the modern leaders of Africa to avert the situation I have just outlined, and by so doing establish new patterns of land use which take into account population growth, the fragility of many semi-arid ecosystems and the inevitability that some steps have to be taken to prevent further degradation of the environment. The tragic famines in the Sahel and Ethiopia are clear pointers to what can happen if leaders allow populations of people and stock to simply multiply without planning. Taking stock to graze in the Kora Reserve provides short-term relief for the hungry; herds that would have perished are saved for a year or two and the numbers increase. But eventually Kora too will be without vegetation and the herds will move on. Sooner or later there will be nowhere further to go, but by then areas such as Kora will have been lost forever. The same pressures can be seen in many parts of Africa and far too often the administrators and politicians are unwilling to take action. I hope that this book and the attention that the Kora Research Project has generated will in a small way be some contribution to the resolution of the crisis.

The area known as Kora is a small, isolated patch of bush dissected by the Tana River. Its genetic diversity and its management problems are but an example of what can be found in many other areas across the great African continent. I personally hope that the humans who are the evolutionary product of the African environment will not be so foolish as to destroy their own background because, by so doing, they are destroying one of their greatest heritages.

Richard Leakey
Kenya

–1–
An Uphill Battle

An astronaut looking down from a satellite on to the African continent would see the huge Sahara desert stretching across the width of the north. To the south of the Sahara there would be a great arc of savanna, starting in West Africa and creeping first eastwards and then south, with a finger stretching into the southwest. These areas of dry bush and desert together make up about 75 per cent of the continent. The rain forests that lie across the Equator are limited to an area in the west, stretching from Sierra Leone in the north to Gabon in the south and the borders of Uganda in the east. These tall dark forests have been drastically reduced in area as a result of population pressure and their clearance for agriculture and timber. At their northern limits the effects of fire and subsistence agriculture, coupled with the use of formerly forested land for pasture, have speeded the southward spread of the Sahel zone, a region frequently featured in the Western media because it is repeatedly ravaged by drought. This zone lies between the true desert of the Sahara and the areas of wooded savanna, and has a vegetation of thorn scrub and sparse grass cover which is easily degraded by herds of domestic stock.

If the astronaut traced the Sahel into the Horn of Africa, he would see that it sweeps down through Somalia and on into eastern Kenya where it peters out close to the southern border with Tanzania. These vast areas, of little value for agriculture, are the home of abundant wildlife and of pastoral tribes. They are characterized by low rainfall and high temperatures, so what little rain does fall is rapidly evaporated. A rainfall map of eastern Africa shows that the area of the Sahel mirrors a large tongue of low rainfall which extends down into Kenya from the north. The so called 'rainfall probability isohyet' indicates that in one year out of ten (10 per cent) precipitation will fall below 250 mm (10 in) per annum within the area enclosed by this line (Figure 2). Passing southwards to the east of Mount Kenya, this tongue of low rainfall crosses the Equator within striking distance of the Tana River. Along the southern bank of this big, brown, muddy river lies the long triangle of land that is the Kora National Reserve.

protection and survival.

In 1980 I had travelled to London to attend an Expeditions Committee of the RGS in Kensington Gore, and dropped into the Expedition Advisory Centre for a chat with Nigel Winser, the RGS Expeditions Officer. Whilst discussing the RGS involvement in expeditions around the world, Nigel sowed the germ of an idea. He had recently met some of the officers of the Kora Wildlife Preservation Trust which had been set up to assist work in the Kora National Reserve, and his feeling was that the Kora National Reserve would be an ideal place to carry out a savanna project. Although I had spent twenty-five years working in most of the major habitats of Kenya, the one area that I had not yet tackled and had long wanted to investigate was the much neglected *Acacia-Commiphora* bush. 'Fine', I said, 'Let's get in touch with people in Nairobi and see if they would be willing to work with us on a joint venture to study the nyika', for I knew that without local assistance and approval it would be impossible to establish a sound logistic base to support a large team in such a remote area.

After our meeting I returned to Oxford and quickly wrote to the Wildlife Conservation and Management Department (WCMD) of the Kenya government, Professor Geoffrey Maloiy of the University of Nairobi, and Richard Leakey, the Director of the National Museums of Kenya, to see if they would be interested in such a joint survey of the Kora National Reserve. Richard replied almost immediately to say that, although there would be many problems regarding Kenyan participation that would need detailed discussion, the National Museum in Nairobi would in principle welcome the idea of such a joint venture with the RGS.

Further preliminary meetings at the RGS in London made it clear that there was a potentially very interesting programme to be conducted in Kora, provided we could finance it and put up a good proposal to the Expeditions Committee and the RGS Council. Such a proposal would have to be a clear and convincing document, for the members of both these committees must be one of the most experienced group of expeditioneers in the world. Over the next year we investigated the sort of work that would be valuable, from which we decided that we should concentrate on building up basic data on the animals and plants of the Reserve. Although one might suppose that it would be most important to establish a management plan for the new Reserve, there is a sad lack of basic descriptive data for virtually all the national parks and reserves in East Africa without which it is impossible to plan sensibly. We were also aware that, whether we scientists like it or not, there are strong socio-political overtones to all planning and management documents. If these are wholly written by outsiders, they often fail to represent local wishes and aspirations. Our preliminary strategy would determine the choice of expedition personnel, and probably the attitudes of the Kenyan authorities. So although planning for the future of Kora was never far from our minds, we decided to concentrate on gathering basic information which we hoped would get the ball rolling and assist the Kenyan authorities in writing a management plan.

The outline plan that evolved was that we should gather together a group that could provide a descriptive inventory of the animal and plant species that occupied the wild country of Kora. From this we could derive a detailed picture of how species were arranged in communities, their geographical distribution and affinities with species in other areas. Careful collection could reveal important information on the abundance or rarity of individual species. Overall, we wanted to aim at building up a picture of the ecology of the Reserve and the relationship of animals and plants to their environment, so the expedition personnel needed to include specialists from all the relevant fields. As well as biologists, we recognized that we would need the assistance of geomorphologists who could explain something of the geology and general physical background, for without the information that these people would be able to give us we could not establish the underlying reasons for the distribution patterns we would observe. We planned to obtain further background on the climate, geology and soils from Kenya government departments who have long-term information on most of these areas, and would be able to fill in most of the data that a comparatively short-term project would not be able to gather in the field. The advance of aerial survey interpretation techniques also indicated that if we were to use satellite images and lower level aerial photography this would add a whole new dimension to the more detailed ground survey that our field team would carry out.

We were also anxious to introduce a time element in the survey, so that it would be possible to show whether changes were taking place and at what rate. Random collection alone would produce a species list, but would not lend itself to future monitoring. The only way to ensure that our work could include a time element in due course would be to establish sample plots on which species and community distribution details could be plotted, so that they could be relocated and examined in the future.

We hoped that the sort of detailed data we had in mind would prove of immense value to the authorities, not just in planning for the future of Kora, but perhaps also to stimulate the establishment of an ecological survey group which would apply the same techniques to other areas, and thereby establish a data bank which could be used in more wide-scale planning operations. It is not uncommon today to hear that an environmental impact statement has been prepared in relation to some newly-proposed development, but unless a detailed inventory is available to provide essential baseline information such documents are of little value. To prepare a management plan for a conservation area requires similar background information, but its terms of reference are much wider than those of an ecological survey and will include consideration of such matters as access for visitors, the planning of roads in relation to local physiography and sites of special interest, staffing (including, where appropriate, anti-poaching control), and accommodation for staff and visitors. The biological background indicates what features are likely to be of special tourist, educational and scientific interest, as well as underlining what measures are likely to be necessary to ensure that habitats are not damaged by visitor pressure, and what species may need to be controlled in terms of their numbers or distribution. Ultimately, like all conservation plans, the decisions taken frequently depend on a cost-benefit analysis, for remote areas with difficult access are expensive to develop in such a way that they are likely to pay for themselves without outside assistance. Without a sound financial base for what is proposed, there is little chance of convincing local people that the 'conservation ethic' can pay for itself.

By mid-1981 we had decided we would plan to take a team to Kenya in 1984, so there was plenty of time to arrange finance, plan a scientific programme and deal with the logistics of political permission, transport and supplies. Getting an expedition off the ground is rather like a rocket taking off on a space mission. At first the rocket seems to move slowly, but it gathers momentum when it is well clear of the ground. Once airborne it soars at tremendous speed, sometimes seemingly out of control, and it is only when the last stage comes, when the satellite is pushed into orbit, that the pilot regains control. Our experience was rather like this, with very slow initial progress, dozens of letters eliciting what seemed to be interminably slow replies.

The promise of support from the National Museums of Kenya was welcome for Richard Leakey and I had been friends since my early teaching days in Kenya. There was virtually no aspect of the National Museum's work and facilities in Nairobi that I was not familiar with, both as a working ecologist and as ex-President of the East African Natural History Society and Trustee of the Museum.

The National Museum's history goes back to 1909 when a group of enthusiastic naturalists met and founded the East Africa and Uganda Natural History Society, publishing their first annual report in 1910. Very quickly the members of the new Society realized that they needed a centre for their proposed activities, so a small two-roomed building was built near the present site of the Nairobi Central Police Station and rented at a cost of £30 a year from a Mr Jevanjee, a Nairobi businessman.

At this time the Museum was wholly owned and run by the Society. The first full-time curator, Mr Arthur Loveridge, took up his duties on 3 January 1915. This was an ideal appointment for this keen herpetologist, whose expertise in the field of reptile studies led later to his appointment as Curator of Reptiles at the famous Museum of Comparative Zoology at Harvard University, where he remained until he retired. His period at the Museum gave it an impetus that has continued ever since, and visitors to Nairobi are still likely to acquire a copy of his guide to the snakes of the highlands.

After World War I, the Society set about raising funds to build a new and larger museum at the top end of Government Road, opposite the site now occupied by the cathedral, and this was opened in 1923. But accommodation was still restricted so further plans were instituted to build the present Museum at the top of Ainsworth Hill, as a memorial to the late Sir Robert Coryndon who was the Governor of Kenya from 1922–5. Increasingly the Natural History Society found it difficult to run the enlarged Museum so, after an enquiry, the suggested that Dr Steve Njuguna would probably be interested in the river research, a field in which he already had considerable local experience. The student side was more difficult for they had all been sent home following the attempted coup in August 1982, shortly before I arrived. None the less, Professor George Kinoti promised to see what he could do and to liaise with Richard Leakey in the Museum.

Whenever I return to Kenya I usually slip in and out quietly, for there are still so many old friends around that it would be very easy to spend my time just saying hello, drinking coffee under the thorn tree outside the New Stanley Hotel, or sipping a cool beer on the verandah of the historic Norfolk Hotel from where safaris have set out since the beginning of the century. There was on this occasion also little time for socializing, but we did go to visit Sandy Price and David Western (another old Nairobi student) at the African Wildlife Foundation, a body that has done so much to support wildlife research in Africa. In fact we discovered David was away, so we left details of our programme so that they knew what we were trying to do. Finally we called on John Sutton of the famous safari firm Ker and Downey, who had been responsible for conducting HRH Prince Charles on his Kenya travels. John had played an important role in the Kenyan phase of Operation Drake, a venture which enabled large numbers of young people from all over the world to experience the thrill of expeditioneering, so we hoped that he and his very experienced colleagues might be interested in our project. When you have travelled the length and breadth of Kenya as I have, there is hardly a spot that you visit, even in the most remote areas, that you do not come across a safari, well ordered and superbly organized, with camps full of 'safari people' who are always welcoming to travellers. We were soon to discover that John, Sol Rabb and their colleagues would be a tower of strength in the later stages of our work, just when they were needed most.

Back at Alex's flat we reviewed our progress and got our lists of information, addresses and telephone numbers in order before we turned our attention to listing the supplies we would need for our visit to George Adamson's camp in Kora in two days time. Even these small lists are important, for once you leave the tarmac and enter the bush, it's too late if you've forgotten anything. We were up early the next morning and after checking the Land Rover drove down to Westlands to fill the tank and spare jerry cans with petrol. We then wandered around the supermarket and the greengrocer's to stock up with essentials and a few goodies to round off a hard day in the bush. All we now needed were our notebooks, binoculars, cameras and collecting gear before we locked the vehicle up for the night in the Museum ready for dawn the next morning when we would head for Kora. I couldn't wait!

– 2 –
Into the Bush

Nairobi lies at 1676 m (5500 ft) above sea level, nestling in a depression on the lower slopes of the eastern highlands that rise steadily towards the eastern wall of the Rift Valley. At this altitude, even on hot days, the thin air is always cool at night, and during most of the year the early mornings are clear. On Saturday, 2 October 1982, Alex, Chum and I made our way out of the city on the road to Thika, which lies 43 km (27 miles) north of Nairobi. The red soil was dark from recent rain, and the coffee and sisal plantations looked refreshed from their soaking, with their leaves shining as if they had just been waxed. The little town of Thika has grown fast in recent years with the development of local light industry, including Land Rover (Kenya) Ltd, who now assemble these sturdy vehicles on the spot. It is perhaps best known for its fruit-processing industry and in particular for its huge fields of pineapples, which produce great mountains of these succulent Central American fruits.

Just before we reached Thika and the Blue Post Hotel, made famous by Elspeth Huxley's *The Flame Trees of Thika*, the road swings in a big arc away from the highland route to Mount Kenya, and travels eastwards past the industrial area and on towards Garissa. This small frontier town lying on the Tana River provides a gateway to the desert-like Northeast Province, and is about four hours drive from the Kora National Reserve. The rain had been patchy, but where it had fallen acacia trees had burst into flower with fragrant spikes and balls of white and yellow mimosa-like flowers, whose sweet scent wafted into the vehicle as we flashed past. The altitude decreases quite rapidly beyond Thika, but large numbers of steep-sided hills still rose sharply from the plains. Prominent among these is Ol Doinyo Sapuk or Kilima ya Mbogu (mountain of the buffalo), a great mass of dolerite like a sleeping whale which is over 2000 m (6600 ft) high. In the early morning it was still shrouded in a fluffy white mass of clouds that sat like a halo around the summit.

The tarmac came sharply to an end 130 km (81 miles) from Nairobi, and we bumped onto the earth road, a great plume of dust rising behind us. Corrugations caused by oscillations set up in the surface by vehicles' wheels stretched

30

across the width of the road, like ripple marks on the sea shore. Oddly enough going slowly shakes vehicles to pieces, but if the corrugations are taken at speed you just float across the top of them, producing a much easier ride. Red dust clothed the bushes along the roadside, giving the immediate countryside an eery, brick-red tone. These bright red soils are characteristic of so many of the arid regions of the world, and are due to oxidization of the iron deposited at the surface as a result of the high rates of evaporation (the process known as laterization). Modern road builders use the iron pan (laterite) that develops near the surface to construct all-weather earth roads. The hard brown nodules are excavated and spread on the surface of the road where they are broken down by the traffic passing over them. As the dry season advances, these roads become more and more corrugated and potholed, but it is not until the rains return and the surface is softened that the local road-maintenance gangs can bring their graders into action to remove the ridges. In some areas, after the sharp tractor-mounted blades have scraped over the road, the job is rounded off by dragging a whole tree behind a tractor to complete the smoothing of the uneven surface. Over much of arid Africa the surface red soils are in large part derived from the action of termites (often incorrectly called white ants), whose mound-building activities have produced a layer of red sorted soil up to 2 m (6 ft) thick.

Ahead of us the road sloped ever downwards, and the landscape was dotted with large groups of hills of all shapes and sizes, from great rounded domes to jagged peaks. At just 210 km (131 miles) from the city we crossed a dry river-bed, with pools and long strips of dark mud from the recent water flow caused by sudden rain showers somewhere far away in the hills. African children were playing in a large pool at the side of the road, and waved enthusiastically as we swung off the road into the little town of Mwingi. This is a typical small African township, with a character all of its own. Small corrugated iron buildings line up on either side of the road – general stores, hardware merchants, bars and restaurants. These shops or dukas are thronged with people who have come to town to sell their goods, buy supplies, or to haggle with a wholesaler to stock their own small shops out in the countryside. For me their atmosphere gives me the feeling of coming home, something I never feel in the big city, where everybody is in a hurry and few folks seem to have time to stop and chat. Here life is at a different pace and you are surrounded by good humour and assistance at every step. As in most countries, if you can speak the local language it is a great help in communicating with the local people, and your acceptance is almost assured. Fortunately my Swahili is still very fluent, even if grammatically questionable, so the three of us were soon on our way to the Moonlight Bar for a beer and a chat with the locals, who told us that rain had fallen on the Kyuso–Kora road in the last two weeks. The modern world has stretched its fingers as far as Mwingi, for the proud bar owner showed us the new room he had just built at the back of his bar to house the local darts club. Perhaps I was not so far from Oxford after all!

Buses were lined up along the road and there were also plenty of local taxis

FAR LEFT, ABOVE *Tiny cocktail ants excavate their homes in the swollen thorn bases of this acacia. The ants defend the tree against attack by insects that eat the foliage and receive nectar in return.*

FAR LEFT, BELOW *Beads of resin collect at the surface of a* Commiphora *that has been slashed by Peter Waterman in his study of these plant products.*

LEFT *Long strands of frankincense resin festoon the trunk of a* Boswellia *tree.*

ABOVE *A line of red-topped sticks marks the position of a transect which has been cut through the dense thorn bush.*

OVERLEAF *A group of Somali camels pause beside a water-hole to drink from a handsomely-carved wooden drinking vessel.*

have played on the African continent, for before their arrival, and that of rice and bananas from Asia, the variety of indigenous foods was small. These included the sorghums and millets, and in West Africa the oil palm (*Elaeis quineensis*) and most varieties of yam (*Dioscorea spp.*). The introductions must have had a profound effect on the very structure of society itself, for they not only provided food materials that could be stored in larger quantities and for longer periods than indigenous food crops, but also enabled the developing agricultural societies to farm in habitats that had previously been closed to them because their altitude, climate or soil did not suit native plants.

The vegetable stalls also carried a wide variety of local plants that are collected and sold as spinaches, while great mounds of sugar cane, an Old World introduction, lay chopped in lengths. Each purchaser indicates the piece he wants, and then wanders away tearing off the sweet sugary interior with his powerful white teeth and discarding small lumps of fibre from which the juice has been extracted. Tomatoes were arranged in neat piles on a piece of sacking, and a large round smiling lady invited me to buy her nyanya, bananas-ndisi, lemons-ndimu, or oranges-muchungwa. Haggling here is a way of life, carried out with a friendly earnestness, and when the bargain has been struck and mama pockets the shillingis, seller and purchaser take leave of each other with a friendly *kwaheri*, each convinced that they have won the encounter.

We were particularly struck by great mounds of brown material piled on a sack, looking for all the world like a yellow-brown soil, but close inspection revealed a jumbled mass of honeycomb, mixed with bees and their larvae. Once extracted, the dark brown, sweet honey has a strong flavour quite unlike any other I have ever tasted. It is strengthened by the blossoms of the acacia and other bush trees and gathered by an army of vicious African bees. The Wakamba are past masters at extracting these from the hollowed-out tree-branch hives that festoon suitable trees like giant festive decorations. Honey was the main sweetener long before the introduction of sugar from the Old World and today it is still widely used. Apart from its value as a food and as an ingredient in native medicine, it is of major importance in brewing the sweet beers of the bush, made from either maize or millet.

At the far end of the market a small group of women sat selling beans of every shape and size, from the familiar red bean or maharagwe, to small black beans with white eyes and various varieties of white beans. These legumes are especially important not only because they are highly nutritious, but also because they can be stored for long periods in a tropical climate, when most other foods would quickly deteriorate.

It is all here on market day, almost anything you might care to buy, from underwear, to a cup and plate, earrings, or a shaving mirror. This variety is no different, I suppose, to what you might find in the UK, but the African market has the very essence of Africa. Here business is taken seriously and is conducted mostly by the women, who often seem to be much easier to communicate with than the men. No doubt a merchant who can't communicate with the customers doesn't do any business.

finance.' Bravely, the committee agreed to my request, for at this stage of the operation we were without funds and quite without the securities that would be required by a bank for such a loan. Briefly we returned to more practical details, and agreed to the formation of a Kora Subcommittee which would oversee the planning of the whole operation. Lieutenant Colonel David Hall, an experienced desert explorer,. consented to being the Chairman, and we agreed that the other members should be invited for their expertise in the fields of expedition health, administration and scientific research. We also proposed the inclusion of Dr Keith Eltringham, the Chairman of the Kora Wildlife Preservation Trust, since his views would provide a line of communication with a body specifically concerned with the Reserve we were to study, and with the work of George Adamson and Tony Fitzjohn.

Before I left London along the M40 motorway, down which I already seemed to have worn a pair of personal grooves, Nigel and I went over the checklist that he had drawn up before I flew to Kenya. We had already started to compile a bibliography for circulation to participants, but we now needed to have talks with Brigadier George Hardy, Deputy Director of the RGS, for it would be essential for us to call on his cartographic resources for the preparation of the Kora base map which would be needed by all the research parties. Above all, though, we needed to draw up a list of commercial concerns and research bodies in the UK who might be interested in contributing to the £55,000 needed to fund the project. A similar list would be required for Kenya, since Nigel was still convinced that some money could be raised there, so we decided to approach the British High Commission for details of British business interests, and for help in tracing American concerns who might be interested in assisting us.

My return to the comparative peace of Oxford left me weary but satisfied that at last we were getting somewhere. Back in the quiet of my study I got down to planning the scientific team, for I had decided that this was something I could do on my own and that there was no need to form a group to plan the scientific programme. It was only possible for me to involve myself closely in the work of the expedition because Nigel Winser would take charge of many of the administrative plans. However, needless to say, if something should go seriously wrong, I remained the guy that would get the flak when the elephant dung started flying. Running an expedition in this way has only been possible since the RGS opened an Expedition Office, partly to assist their own projects, but more particularly to provide information for smaller expeditions organized by young people through the Expedition Advisory Centre. Indeed, the establishment of this unique organization and its planning seminars has led to a massive increase in the number of expeditions, and also to a higher standard of work in the field. Frequently, of course, expedition leaders do not have specific expertise in all the scientific aspects of their projects, but I personally felt more comfortable in attempting to play the leading role in the establishment of our research aims, rather than immersing myself in purely organizational aspects.

When an expedition is planned, it is not uncommon for a leader to select participants from a wide variety of people who apply to be included. In our case, however, I was anxious to build my UK team from biologists I already knew to have had experience in Africa, and more particularly in East Africa, for this would ensure that their background knowledge would enable them to go straight into the field and start work immediately, without the need for intensive familiarization with the local flora and fauna. In my view this is particularly important when a team has limited time in the field, and mutual confidence and social harmony is always much more likely when a team are at least familiar with each other's work.

My earlier proposal to the RGS had outlined the areas that I felt would need detailed investigation in order to provide an ecological and taxonomic description of the Kora flora and fauna. It was therefore not too difficult to work out who I would need to complement the National Museum team I had already had talks with in Nairobi. All the time, however, I was well aware that, the larger the UK team, the more it would cost in terms of air fares and the transport of materials. With this proviso in mind, the participants had to be selected for the following major areas of study:

1 *Satellite studies* In my initial planning I was aware of the need to establish background information on the landforms and vegetation of the Kora area as a necessary basis for any of the more detailed work, especially that on the animals. I was very aware that enhanced Landsat satellite images contained a mass of information which would be a vital contribution to our ground survey work, something we had already seen on our preliminary print from Nairobi. In particular, satellite images taken regularly during the course of our studies would help us monitor seasonal changes in the Reserve. I also knew that the value of these images would be greatly increased if we could have an experienced satellite team from NASA in the field to carry out 'ground truth' studies that would help both them and us in interpreting these mysterious images from space.

2 *Geomorphology* In any ecological field study, information on the physical background is absolutely essential, for both vegetation and animal life are ultimately dependent on the nature of the country in which they occur. Fortunately, Dr Andrew Goudie (who has recently been appointed to the Chair of Geography of the School of Geography in Oxford) had wide experience in studying landform problems in the arid tropics, so he and his co-workers made a natural team who would travel to Kenya before the main party so that their research would be available before the rest of the expedition started. Andrew's long association with the RGS was an additional asset and he was also a member of the Kora Planning Subcommittee.

3 *River studies* The importance of dam developments on the Tana River made it vital that we should have a strong group to study the Tana River's water chemistry and physical conditions. We knew we would be able to call on Dr

Humphrey Greenwood and his staff at the British Museum (Natural History) in South Kensington for assistance in fish identification, while the presence of Dr Steve Njuguna at the University of Nairobi meant that we could rely on the Nairobi team to enlist his aid for this important side of our work, so I was confident that in this area we had sufficient specialist expertise on tap.

4 *Vegetation* Although many members of our team would primarily be involved in taxonomy (the identification of animals and plants), the overriding interest of us all would be the ecology of the Kora National Reserve. Understanding this involved interpreting the distribution and abundance of all the constituent species in the major habitat types, and the way in which they interrelated. The botanically-oriented members therefore needed to make up several interlocking teams to work in the following specific areas:

Vegetation survey Just as we needed a geomorphological survey before we started our studies, a survey of the major habitat types related to dominant soil cover would provide the baseline for the study of Kora's ecology. We had recently heard that Dr Murray Watson and Chris Hemming, who had conducted the South Turkana Expedition's vegetation survey, were working in Somalia and would be willing to come down to Kora with their light aircraft to carry out the vital air and ground survey of the vegetation.

Studies of the plant mass supported per unit area Feeling happy that the broad survey work was guaranteed, I now needed to ensure that we had information that would indicate the quantities of plant material that are to be found in Kora and what there is that would provide a potential food source for the herbivorous fauna. Following my discussions with KREMU in Kenya, the decision about who should be involved wasn't difficult. The survey I had in mind requires large numbers of people to carry out the field work so I was quite happy that we should reiterate to KREMU's Director, Dr David Andere, that we would like their help. I was, however, well aware that they were very short of funds themselves, even in respect of such essential items as fuel for their aircraft and vehicles.

Taxonomic studies The Royal Botanic Gardens at Kew had expressed an interest in receiving plant specimens from Kora, but we agreed that the distinguished Herbarium in Nairobi could provide all the expertise we would need to both collect and subsequently identify our plant specimens. Kew's offer of a quantity of expensive plant-drying papers was gratefully received, for the less we had to buy, the less money we had to raise.

Vegetation community structure Having planned how we would study habitat distribution in broad terms, it was now necessary to fill in the detail. Here I had no problem, for Dr Andrew Agnew of the University College of Wales in Aberystwyth had been a colleague in Nairobi and was the author of the very valuable *Upland Wild Flowers of Kenya*, as well as being a good ecologist who had worked in the very similar country of the Tsavo (East) National Park. I had already had a quick telephone conversation with him in which he had told me that he would be delighted to look at habitat structure and, far more important, establish a series of standard plots which would form the basis of sampling by other groups. He also felt sure he could provide an assistant, should it be necessary.

Plant gums and resins These apparently barren wildernesses of thorn bush seem to have little value, but in fact, as I have already described, they contain natural plant products that we felt might have commercial potential. Species producing resin and gum are common in Kenya (we expected to find up to fifteen in Kora), but they are currently hardly used commercially. We felt that a study of these phytochemical materials might produce results that could have important commercial applications, such as the discovery of antiseptic properties or qualities of use in perfumery. More particularly, however, we recognized the need to find commercial uses for natural products that could provide an income for local people, and more importantly, perhaps, that would improve the economy while at the same time protecting these delicate environments. Here again we were fortunate, for Dr Peter Waterman of Strathclyde University in Scotland is a pharmaceutical chemist who has become a phytochemist with a special interest in those plant characteristics which affect their predation by animals. Peter had already chuckled at the thought of returning to Kenya, so the plant team was complete.

5 *Animals* To a large degree the animal programme would be a survey of species found in Kora, together with estimates of their numbers and pattern of distribution to complete the ecological picture. The work groups involved could be planned taxonomically, since zoologists tend to be authorities on their own particular favourites and are sometimes almost pathologically partisan. Hence my task was to find individuals or parties to tackle the following major animal groups.

Invertebrates The study of these generally small animals raised enormous problems, for they are incredibly numerous. The insects were undoubtedly the dominant group and here we could utilize the expertise of the Nairobi team: this included Martin Pickford who was an authority on molluscs and Alex Mackay who had a long-standing interest in scorpions. In addition we would have the assistance of Dr Mark Ritchie, who had arrived at the Museum just before I left on secondment from the Centre for Overseas Pest Research in London. He had been given the specific task of building up the Museum's taxonomic collections of insects so that they could provide a pan-African identification service, especially for insects of economic importance. It appeared that it might be difficult to find anybody in the UK who could help with identification, so we felt the most useful addition to this team would be a biologist with tropical experience, a scientist who knew his insects but would also be interested in the conservation angle. Dr Mark Collins fitted the bill well. After his time as an undergraduate with us in Oxford, he had obtained a PhD working on termites in Nigeria, had later worked on termites in Nairobi and had been a member of the RGS Mulu Expedition. He had recently joined the International Union for the Conservation of Nature's Data Monitoring

Unit in Cambridge, where they had just published the first Red Data Book on endangered invertebrates. Provided his unit would allow him leave, he could join the strong invertebrate team.

Vertebrates Because these large creatures are not very numerous in terms of numbers of species and individuals, from a zoological point of view they are relatively less significant. However, their importance in terms of tourism and conservation meant that they were a vital element in our survey. Here again we would have few problems finding people for our team, for in East Africa I sometimes feel there are more biologists than the animals they study. The individuals or groups were selected on taxonomic lines.

Fish In Nairobi I had learned that Dr Ken Campbell, a Kenya-born zoologist, had recently obtained his PhD studying birds and fish in Lake Malawi, and although he was to take a job as an ecological consultant locally, he would be able to join us in the field. Since he could not be with us for the whole period, it would be necessary to include two other less experienced people who could handle the heavy seine nets and continue to collect when Ken was absent. Fortunately, my Kenya-born son Christopher and his friend Michael Saunders were both very keen on fish and were between school and university, so they were told to get busy raising money for their air fares and subsistence. This sent them both scuttling off to the Job Centre from which Mike emerged as a vegetable salesman and Chris as a male home help.

Amphibians and reptiles I felt the frogs and toads ought to be of particular interest in Kora, but I knew that their activity would be very seasonal. The reptiles should be less seasonal and would include crocodiles, tortoises, terrapins, monitors (a type of lizard), chameleons, lizards and snakes. Alex Mackay was the National Museum's herpetologist so he was an immediate choice to head this group, with possible further assistance from Dr Jim Hebrard at the University of Nairobi, and from a Swedish snake expert from Lund who was developing techniques for assessing the abundance of these reptiles in arid areas of Africa.

Birds The avifauna of these dry bush habitats is surprisingly rich. For identification we were relying on Chum van Someren from the Museum. I knew he would have a difficult job but that he would be able to call on the assistance of his staff, who were very experienced in the field.

Mammals Kora was likely to be rich in both large and small mammals, a somewhat arbitrary division of these fascinating creatures. Issa Aggundey in the National Museum was an authority on bats, but I needed an ecologist with a special interest in the numerous small rodents. Dr Sky Alibhai had graduated at Makerere in Uganda and, shortly after he joined us in Oxford to do a PhD, his family were thrown out of the country. Now at Bedford College, London, he not only knew about rodents, but had worked on the African species when he was in Uganda, so we asked him to assist with the collection of the major species and to use the project to continue his own special interest in their reproduction.

The dense bush of Kora was not likely to have the abundant large mammal fauna that might be expected on the grass plains, but the species that did occur were full of interest. Rather than add a further member to the UK team we decided that we should rely on assistance in this area from the WCMD, with all other members of the project providing information on the numbers of large mammals and their distribution from sightings made during their other work and travel about the Reserve.

6 *Inselbergs* The only areas that would receive special attention were the rocky inselbergs that stand out from the bush like stony islands. We knew that they supported large numbers of endemic species, isolated by considerable distances from similar species. Although I would clearly need assistance from all the other groups, I had already decided that I should undertake this special study and seek funds to finance it.

Having agreed on our team and established that everyone would be available, we circulated all expedition members with details of the plans and asked them to complete documentation that would give us full information on their qualifications and scientific publications, copies of which could be forwarded to Nairobi for research clearance through Richard Leakey's office. Additionally we asked for a joining fee to assist with administrative costs, and for details of medical histories, blood groups, and even dietary fads. A final document prepared at the RGS was an agreement that we asked all members to sign concerning the copyright of photographs and the publication of both scientific and popular results. Such agreements sometimes cause difficulties, which is precisely why they need to be written carefully, so that publicity is channelled centrally and post-expedition publications can proceed smoothly.

Our original proposal to the RGS was now rewritten as a full description of the work in a form that could be used in fund raising and publicity. The name Kora Research Project 1983 had been adopted and Nigel suggested that we should design a logo that could be used on our notepaper, sweat shirts and other material that would be circulated. We had been quite keen on using the diminutive dik-dik, the commonest antelope in Kora, but when we approached the brilliant wildlife artist and zoologist, Jonathan Kingdon, he immediately produced some delightful sketches of the yellow-billed hornbill, a small but captivating occupant of Kora. This male hornbill still graces our documents, with his head held back, and his neck pouches half inflated as he calls.

Nigel's office was under great pressure, for the Kora project was but a small part of their total responsibilities. Although he and his charming wife Shane kept things moving along with lists of cash received and needed, movements of people and supplies and the whole paraphernalia of expedition planning, it was clear we needed more help. Fortunately, the RGS seems to act as a magnet for willing volunteers who work long hours for the love of the ethic of the dedicated expeditioneer. Nicola Bennett-Jones, who had already had experience as a nurse on other expeditions, now travelled to the office several days a week to organize medical supplies under the guidance of our doctor, Bent Juel-Jensen, a distinguished physician at the Radcliffe Infirmary in Oxford. Deborah

Boys, who had helped the office for some time, took over as secretary of our Planning Subcommittee, and started to type the long lists of Kora flora and fauna that arrived from Nairobi on to the newly installed word processor. Nigel also obtained the further assistance of Michael Keating and Hamish Hay, who took charge of marshalling and packing equipment, visiting potential donors, and chasing up contacts all over the place.

The UK research team prepared applications for funds to just about every possible source we could think of, while I prepared further requests to be sent to the Royal Society, the Overseas Development Administration, the National Geographic Society and numerous smaller bodies. The deadlines for these applications had become extremely tight, and the RGS President, Sir Vivian Fuchs, spent hours sitting in his office signing letters and application forms, all in the hope that at least a small percentage of them might yield a positive response.

The time whistled by and on 18 December 1982 Nigel Winser flew back to Nairobi for a planning visit, to arrange for the considerable back-up that would be necessary to sustain us in the field. His first reactions on arrival were pessimistic in the extreme, for Richard Leakey now considered that no local finance would be available to sustain the Museum's involvement in the project, while lack of really positive commitment from the WCMD seemed to indicate possible problems with obtaining the all-important political permission. Fortunately, Nigel, huge briefcase in hand, is a powerful persuader, and his second letter to me was more cheerful, especially after what was for him a nostalgic pilgrimage to Kora and George's camp which he had previously visited in 1976. Jock Anderson of East African Safaris Ltd provided him with transport in Nairobi, and the Cooper Motor Corporation (the Land Rover agents) with a vehicle for the safari. Above all he felt, as I had in October, that, whatever the problems, we had to press on with our plans to protect that amazing bushland wilderness from the pressures it was now facing. This visit to Kora merely enhanced the excitement that had already been generated amongst people in London, and in the National Museum in Nairobi.

Nigel's comparatively short visit must have been even more exhausting than mine, for by the time he returned to London on 4 January 1983 he had discussed political permission, project membership, local public relations, the construction of a base camp or camps, and medical support from the Flying Doctor Service and the Nairobi Hospital. The results of this mammoth task were presented at the third meeting of the Kora Planning Subcommittee on 2 February in a 32-page document which covered all the topics already mentioned, as well as financial contacts with Barclays Bank, British Airways, Cooper Motor Corporation, Guinness, and Ker and Downey Safaris. This report set the scene accurately and in some respects made depressing reading, for we were only too aware that promises are never a reality until they are expressed in terms of cash, goods or action. We had, however, already put out all the feelers that we could into the world of finance, and we now faced the difficult period when there is little more that can be done other than to wait and see. At this point in the proceedings, I had to disappear to southern Africa to fulfil a long-standing engagement to study acacia trees and the dispersal of their seeds by large mammals. Although I felt guilty about this trip at the time, it held us in good stead in Kora where there were many of the same species. In my absence Andrew Goudie occupied the hot seat, answering questions and encouraging those in the RGS office who leapt on the incoming mail each morning in the hope that it contained cash or a promise of help. Fortunately no huge crises arose before I returned to London in March.

It had become apparent during Nigel's talks with people in Kenya that we would not be able to import goods into the country for the project without incurring crippling duty, so although we were generously being offered large quantities of food and materials manufactured in the UK, they would have to be left out of our plans. This information was neither surprising nor unfair, for developing nations are as anxious to persuade visitors to spend their money locally as we are in our own country. In the case of some items, however, the question of duty did raise problems, for many materials we would need are not produced in Kenya, and would have to be purchased locally at greatly inflated prices. Fortunately it was possible to import scientific goods into Kenya free of duty for use in association with the National Museum, which would ease some of our financial and administrative burdens. Land Rover Ltd had pressed ahead with their generous plans to loan us four of their new 110s, and in addition had delegated two of their engineers to accompany us to service them and monitor their performance in the field. This plan entailed a mass of new administrative problems, for the vehicles had to be insured, transported to Kenya, and legal documentation arranged which would enable us to import them free of duty until the end of the 1983 season. In the event that they were not re-exported by May 1984, the Director of the RGS signed, with a shaking hand, an indemnity which guaranteed the payment of £25,000 on each vehicle should we fail to comply with the agreement.

Along with these heavy vehicles there was the accumulating mass of equipment that began to arrive at Kensington Gore, ranging from small-mammal traps, to tubes, plastic bags and an electro-fisher which had been loaned by the manufacturers in Ireland to help with the Tana River fish survey. With generous assistance from General Chappell and Lieutenant Colonel Steve Gilbert (both members of the RGS Council), we discovered that a number of RAF airlifts would be taking place to Kenya shortly before the project was due to begin, so liaison was initiated through Sir Vivian Fuchs, the President, and Dr John Hemming, the Director. This finally cleared the hurdle of how the vehicles would be transported, and a quantity of scientific equipment could also travel in them. By now time was running out, so Saturday mornings saw the arrival of bands of helpers who congregated at the RGS to complete the exciting task of packing.

At the same time we were having further correspondence with the Kenyans, for on my return to Oxford in March we still did not have a formal agreement with the WCMD. We needed their permission to carry out our work in Kora and also to build a camp that could accommodate our team. Fortunately the necessary agreement arrived soon afterwards. The Department offered to station an APU team with us for protection during our stay, but also asked that we should build a permanent camp that would be handed over to them on the completion of our research. This we readily agreed on condition that the camp would be available to the project at any future date that we might wish to carry out further studies. Fortunately, at this point Richard Leakey passed through London on his way to America, so we were able to thrash out some of the unfinished details, especially in respect of government liaison and agreements, before he rushed back to Heathrow.

Not least amongst our preoccupations at this time was to ensure that this new RGS venture received adequate publicity. Even if this did not benefit us directly, it would help to publicize the importance of these joint initiatives that were increasingly being sponsored by the RGS as an aid to the Developing World. We had already arranged for newspaper articles with brief press releases, but much more encouraging was the fact that the *Observer* had expressed interest in material for a colour supplement, largely due to the persistence of Dr John Hemming. Although this would entail the addition of Victoria Southwell as a photographer, it would ensure wide exposure and the production of suitable pictures to satisfy our growing number of sponsors. Also, the fee that we would get would aid our still meagre financial resources. Further encouragement in the public relations field came from Peter Jones of the BBC Natural History Unit's 'World About Us' team. He told us they were contemplating a film about environmental problems in Kenya, and especially the work of UNEP, in which our own project could be used as a natural backdrop to the story of environments grossly disturbed by mankind. Radio programmes for the overseas service of the BBC were another avenue for our ideas, although they took up valuable time that was still needed to raise funds.

Still feeling that we had not quite reached the point of no return, even if our work was to be under-funded, our official launching ceremony on 14 April came as something of a shock. I found myself surrounded by our team and a crowd of pressmen who took dozens of photographs and cooed with admiration at the smart, blinding white Land Rovers that had been driven down from Birmingham. Somehow it all seemed too easy as I addressed the distinguished company in the RGS lecture hall, for here was an immense amount of goodwill towards what we were trying to do, but little money with which to pay our mounting bills. None the less, it was encouraging, and drove us all on to further efforts before the point of final commitment when the giant transport plane would take off from southern England to lift our vehicles and equipment to Kenya.

The next meeting of the Planning Subcommittee was to consider progress in fund raising, and there were sighs of relief when they heard that we had finally obtained grants to support the rock-outcrop, tree-resin, and small-mammal studies. The RGS then generously offered us £4500 left in the South Turkana Expedition fund, which the leader, Dr Michael Gwynne, had agreed we might use. Michael's recent visit to America from the GEMS unit in Nairobi had brought the welcome news that NASA had agreed to take special satellite images of Kora for us, which would be interpreted by Drs Brent Holben and Chris Justice at the Goddard Space and Flight Center in Washington, both of whom were anxious to join us in Kora in August.

In spite of the good news, we still had to obtain a major grant, and approaches to the National Geographic Society, the World Bank and the Overseas Development Administration had been unsuccessful. In the latter case, however, we persisted by preparing a further detailed application concentrating particularly on the geomorphological survey to be carried out by Andrew Goudie in mid-May. This Dr John Hemming and Sir Vivian Fuchs agreed to submit on our behalf. Indeed, if it had not been for these stalwart supporters in London, the grant from the Overseas Development Administration, our air transport, and other fund-raising efforts might well have foundered all together.

Lieutenant Colonel Gilbert cheered us all further by reporting that the Defence Adviser, Colonel Doyle, and the Commanding Officer of BATLSK (British Army Training Liaison Staff Kenya), Colonel Bob Harrison, had arranged for a group to study the logistics of constructing a base camp on the Tana River, with further assistance in the shape of Sergeant Bill Inglis and Corporal Tom Hampson who would be seconded to the project in May to help with the construction of the camp. Thus, although we had made no final decisions regarding the exact size of the camp, and the procurement of materials, it at last looked as if we could complete the planning phase. The only decision still to be made was when Nigel should return to Nairobi to supervise the final arrangements: it seemed vital that he should do this at the beginning of May. Tim Palmer, an Oxford zoology graduate, would go out for the month of June to finish off the camp's construction, and Mike Keating and Hamish Hay in mid-June to take some of the load in a final effort of local fund raising.

Shortly after Nigel left for Kenya the vehicles were transported over, even though in a final assessment of our financial position we seriously considered cancelling the whole venture as we felt we could hardly justify the risk that we might be facing the RGS with a large deficit. Indeed, it was only Nigel's assurance from Kenya that he was convinced we could raise some money there, and a strong statement of support from the RGS Council, that averted what in retrospect we realize would have been an over-cautious response to our position. Indeed, looking back, I sigh with relief when I wonder what final nudge it was that made us say: 'Go ahead. It will be alright on the night.'

In the UK there was frantic activity as the team dashed around collecting last items of equipment, booking their flights with British Airways, and standing in line to have their arms filled with inoculations against most of the ills you could think of, and several we had hardly heard of. More money dribbled in and the Bursar at the RGS looked at our balance sheet more favourably. For me and the other university members, it was also the end of another academic year and final-examination time when gowns and caps were of more immediate concern than shorts and a safari hat.

Out in Kenya the lorries pulled out of Nairobi loaded with poles, wire, hessian, cement and tools en route for the rough bush roads and the site of our future home. Unlike building schemes in the UK, where planning permission may take months, in Kora Sergeant Inglis and Corporal Hampson had a site marked out, post holes dug and the roof started within a week. By the time they left the water tank was up and the first fence nearing completion as the merry band of local Korakora people showed how good they were at building Adamson-style dwellings. No sooner had they pulled out than Tim Palmer arrived to enlist the aid of the redoubtable Terence Adamson to complete the construction. He worked amid the paraphernalia of a construction site, with lions patrolling up and down at night just outside the incomplete perimeter wire, while a large crocodile took a Somali goat on the other bank of the river, just opposite the camp. Tim renewed his acquaintance with the Swahili language that he had learnt while working with me on dung beetles in the Tsavo National Park, and must have lost half a stone in weight having 'the time of his life', as he told me when he returned at the end of June, just before I left. I made my way to Heathrow wondering if it really all looked as wonderful as he described, but I needn't have worried, for Tim is not given to exaggeration, just an infectious enthusiasm for all things African. It's a disease you cannot be inoculated against, and it's called 'a love of Africa'.

eastern boundary of the Kora National Reserve. It lies just below the first set of rapids on the river upstream from the coast, the point at which further navigation was impossible, just as the inhospitable waterless bush either side of the river formed an equally impenetrable route.

Shortly after Peters' attempt to explore the Tana, J.R.W. Piggott was sent by the Imperial British East Africa Company to explore the route into the interior, driven no doubt by the news of German presence on the river. Piggott immediately travelled to Malindi to raise a safari. With the assistance of Mohammed bin Hamar, he gathered together 5 headmen, an interpreter, 2 servants and 180 porters and askaris, with a promise of further assistance from Galla (Oroma) guides by the Liwali of Malindi.

Piggott's safari set out from Golbanti on the Tana river delta on 1 March 1889 and travelled through the lower river basin, where the local Wapokomo people were being continually harassed by the Somalis in the north and the Masai in the south. It took them another month to march from Kidori to Korokoro (the Ola or Oda Boruruwa of Peters), where Piggott refers to a lake or swamp around which there were numerous small villages. This point on the river marks the edge of the main slope down from the highlands, and beyond the last falls the Tana flows out on to a vast alluvial plain which stretches from here to the coast. At this point also, the riverine vegetation suddenly broadens into a wide forest strip, which is dissected by meanders and backwaters. It is at this point today that the village of Osako lies on the edge of the Reserve.

From Korokoro, Piggott struck inland into the dense bush and recorded the presence of numerous quartz reefs which littered the land as far as he could see. He recorded a particularly large hill or outcrop which he called Kulumba (a common coastal name). From its position on his map this is almost certainly the large outcrop of Kumbulanwa, which lies at the southern end of the Kora Reserve. Thus, as Piggott passed on to Mumoni and Ngomeni, and finally back to the coast via the Yatta plateau, he provided the first description of the nyika bush of the upper Tana river basin in which the Kora National Reserve lies, isolated and surrounded by a protective wall of thorn scrub.

Two years after Piggott's exploration, the stern wheel steamer *Kenya* carrying Captain F.G. Dundas, Ernest Gedge and C.W. Hobley was used to map the lower course of the Tana up to Hamaye where they established a camp. Hobley considered that, from the lower Hargezo Falls (the modern Kora Falls) at Korokoro, the river was like a 'mini-Nile' as it flowed over the great alluvial plain, and he noted particularly the extensive meanders and well developed forest. He also observed that the broad belt of forest, fringed by acacias, doum palms, wild figs and the unique Tana River poplar (*Populus denhardtiorum*, now called *P. ilicifolia*), stopped at the point where the alluvial materials met the weathered quartzites at Korokoro.

Hobley, the expedition geologist, was a good observer who included brief descriptions of the fauna and flora in his account of the journey published in the *Journal* of the RGS in 1894. In particular, he noted the abundance of crocodiles all along the river they surveyed, and also commented that these creatures were extensively hunted by the local people for food but that he declined to taste them. His records of fish were brief but he does comment that catfish were abundant and reached 20 kg (45 lb), but that they were quite inedible. The bright silver dace he records were almost certainly one of the several species of *Barbus* that are common in the Tana, although the small predatory *Alestes* are also of similar colour. The only other fish he noted was the minnow, a reference to the African top minnow (*Engraulicypris*). These are now rather infrequent but Hobley refers to them as being very abundant.

Records of mammals were maintained all along the river and it is interesting to note that most of the species found today did not appear to become common until Korokoro. The arid-country Beisa oryx was quite absent until the expedition reached the middle reaches of the Tana, which is in some ways surprising since this handsome antelope is really an animal of open scattered bush with a moderate grass cover. However, this pattern of distribution may be explained by Hobley's observation that hunting by local tribes had had a considerable effect on the elephant population in the lower reaches and that these animals only became common in the Korokoro area where the dense bush made hunting difficult. Indeed it is interesting to speculate that the Kora area provided a secure refuge for wildlife even at this time.

After the journey of the steamship *Kenya*, many other parties travelled up this river, both by water and on foot, frequently reaching the Hargezo (Kora) Falls. The best account of the late nineteenth century is that of the Reverend R.M. Ormerod, a United Free Church missionary from the Golbanti mission near the river's mouth, who set out on 19 August 1895. It took him just over five weeks to reach Korokoro, where he recorded that the local people were like the Pokomo close to his mission but that they spoke an Oroma language and referred to themselves as Munyo Yaya. At Oda Boruruwa in the Korokoro area he also observed that the people lived on an island, a position which gave them considerable protection from attack by neighbouring tribes. Above Korokoro, Reverend Ormerod travelled by canoe for about nine hours to reach the Hargezo Falls, which his map of the district shows located just to the west of 39°E. Amazingly, this position is almost exactly the same as that recorded on modern maps, confirming that the Hargezo Falls are indeed the Kora Falls. The Korokoro area shown on Ormerod's map, and described by other travellers before him, can be identified on the Saka map of the Kenya Survey which lies immediately to the east of the Kora sheet. At this point on the map there is a small crescentic meander to the north of the main course of the river which isolates an island of land. The local people still live on this small piece of land and take their animals to graze north and south of the Tana.

Despite the innumerable difficulties experienced by these early travellers, and the crude methods of survey available to them, the detail provided on their maps makes it quite easy to identify major physical features. Village names, however, are not easy to reconcile with present-day settlements since those recorded on these early maps almost certainly referred to small groups of transient habitations belonging to pastoralists, which lasted for a few years at the most. The term or locality of Korokoro is still of particular interest for, although no such place is found on modern maps, the local Oroma people refer to themselves as the Korakora. Clearly one of the major problems in interpreting the early records is that the explorers seldom spoke the local language, and when they employed interpreters they were usually not of the same tribe as the locals, or even perhaps coast Arabs who provided their own names for both places and people.

The Korakora are Oroma (pronounced Orma) speakers, mistakenly called Galla by all the early explorers who did not realize that this was the Arab name for the people in the interior, and that the true Galla are similar people who came down from Somalia. The Oroma belong to the much larger group called the Borana who are thought to have migrated from the Ethiopian Highlands between 1660 and 1720, forsaking their agricultural practices and becoming pastoralists. Today the Oroma are largely cattle people, while the Borana north of the Tana have taken to keeping camels in their much more arid surroundings. The question of tribal terminology is complicated by the fact that the northern Borana refer to the Oroma as Wardaa, and although all these groups (including the Galla) are related, they have been separated long enough for their languages and customs to diverge considerably. The major group of Borana peoples still live in Ethiopia where they make up 50 per cent of the nation's population.

Although travel became easier after this period of early exploration, there have been few accounts since then of the nyika bush that fringes the Tana. This does not mean that the area was unknown, but the hunters, naturalists and administrators who knew it well have in most cases left behind no records of their impressions and observations.

It was not until 1976 that another expedition took up the challenge to explore the Tana from its upper reaches to the sea. This was the Polytechnic of Central London Tana River Expedition, led by Nigel Winser, who was now back in Kenya with the Kora project. His group of young people floated down the river in large dinghies, sometimes hurtling over terrifying rapids and cataracts. They collected specimens and carried out ecological studies from temporary camps which they erected en route, all the time working closely with the local Kenyans.

The first of these temporary camps was on a sandy, wooded island opposite Kora Rock and about 30 km (19 miles) downstream from our new base camp. Their next camp was on a lovely site among doum palms and towering acacias about 40 km (25 miles) further downstream, and was called Korakora after the very friendly local people. So, ninety years after the first outsiders came to this area, the name that was used in those accounts written so long ago appears once again.

During the course of planning the Polytechnic of Central London Tana River Expedition 1976, these young people called on the advice of George Adamson who characteristically came to their aid immediately, just as he was to welcome us seven years later. The hospitality of those that dwell in the African bush is legendary, and we were aware of it even though we had only been in Kora for a few hours. But perhaps the oddest feeling for me was the sense of tranquillity that I had in the bush, for although one must be ever vigilant against the potential dangers in this wild country, providing you do not take advantage of either man or beast, you are almost certainly in greater danger of being run over by a bus on Magdalen Bridge in Oxford than you are from the perils of the bush. So, although I had sat at London Airport listing all the dangers in my mind, I fell instantly to sleep as soon as my head hit the pillow on our first night in Kora, and continued to do so until we left. Even though the roar of a distant lion, or the whoop-whoop of a hyaena would bring me briefly to consciousness, I would go back to sleep reassured that Africa was still out there, as it has always been.

There is only one time to rise in the bush, and that is before 6 am, when it is still cool and you can hear the wildlife waking up. On our first morning we had to allocate priorities for vehicles, and since Steve Njuguna was only with us for two weeks, it was essential that we should get him moving without delay. Steve is a tall, good-looking, bespectacled guy with a good knowledge of freshwater biology, so the aim was that he should look at as many aquatic habitats as possible before he returned to Nairobi. There were hot springs, salt springs, water-holes and sand luggas to be studied, but paramount in our interests was the Tana which conveniently bubbled past virtually at our feet.

The history of the rivers and lakes of East Africa is complex, but is inextricably woven into the landscape's geological history. During the Pliocene and Pleistocene periods, which together span a period of about eleven million years, the surface of Africa was lifted, folded and torn asunder by intense earth movements and volcanic activity. The largest of these movements was that which resulted in the formation of the Great Rift Valley, a massive groove in the Earth which runs down the continent from the Middle East to Malawi, where it peters out. Before the formation of the Rift Valley the land was at a level of little more than 600 m (2000 ft) and the major rivers of Africa flowed westwards into the Congo system, but when the Rift and its accompanying highlands were formed, several rivers began to flow eastwards into the Indian Ocean and were invaded by marine creatures like the eels and gobies. But the original configuration is still apparent in the affinities between the fish faunas of rivers flowing to east and west. Over such a long period of time, of course, there have been considerable variations in the climate, and the water flow in rivers such as the Tana has altered greatly. During wet phases the rivers have deposited large areas of alluvium, while they have been reduced to little more than a seasonal trickle during periods when the climate was dry. There has also been considerable volcanic activity since the Rift was formed, for the massive lavas of Mount Kenya are little more than three million years old, while smaller vents and flows have redirected river courses, and even separated them altogether, as is clear in the case of the Yatta plateau that now divides the Tana and Galana rivers.

74   As was outlined in Chapter 1, one of the original reasons for coming to the

Kora National Reserve was to study the effects of dam construction upstream and the likely impact of projected plans for further dams. In the late 1960s four dams had been constructed on the upper reaches of the Tana to provide hydroelectric power for Kenya's developing industries as an alternative to oil-powered stations: Masinga (whose impounded waters cover an area of 120 km², 46 sq miles), Kamburu, Gitarru and Kindarume. Kiambere, planned to be as massive as Masinga, is still under construction and a further five dams are planned to be built downstream over the next fifteen to twenty years, the last two of which will be sited at Adamson's Falls in the North Kitui Reserve, just beyond Kora's western boundary, and at the Kora Falls. The area to be impounded by the dam at the Kora Falls will affect the ecosystem of the whole Reserve. The impact of this dam will not necessarily be deleterious, but it is clearly important that such large-scale developments go hand in hand with soundly-based ecological studies. We did not imagine that we could solve all the difficulties associated with this development, but we hoped we would be able to draw attention to the effects and emphasize major problems.

In addition to the provision of hydroelectric power, the taming of the Tana River waters has also led to their being extensively utilized for irrigation, both upstream at Mwea-Tebere and downstream at the Bura Irrigation Settlement Project. At Bura, 12,000 hectares (30,000 acres) are being brought into cultivation and there are plans to extend the scheme to 17,000 hectares (42,500 acres). Clearly irrigation is vital to the development of agriculture in Kenya, but the impoundment of further water in new dams will alter the pattern of flow on the Tana and this may well have profound effects in the lower reaches of the river. In particular, the dams are likely to have a major impact on natural habitats, including the broad riverine forests which are the home of the endemic Tana River colobus monkey and the Tana River mangabey. The future of these species is already endangered by the pressures on their environment from the tenant farmers on the irrigation scheme, who use the forest as a source of construction materials and firewood. The recognition of these problems was the principal reason for the studies by Francine Hughes, and the team funded by the Dutch government.

Before we travelled further afield, Steve marshalled members of the team to measure profiles of the river bottom close to camp. This seemed quite easy until we launched George Adamson's and Ken Campbell's boats into the water. The river flows at a steady 3 km (2 miles) an hour and even the outboards had to work hard against the current as their occupants stretched a line across the turbulent waters. Having secured the line on the far bank and concluded that the river varied from 100 to 137 m (320 to 450 ft) in width, Steve then measured the depth of water at intervals below the line and found that the deepest channel was 2.4 m (8 ft). Measuring the flow rate raised bigger problems. One boat was anchored in the sandy bottom, and the second held downstream by a line. The flow rate was then measured by calculating the speed of a floating object as it passed between the two boats. All would have been well had the occupants of the first boat not let go the line and we saw the second boat go

75

Engraulicypris

Gnathocnemus

Barbus

Sarotherodon spilurus

Eutropius

Alestes

Petrocephalus

Synodontis

Anguilla

Mormyrus

Glossogobius

Labeo

Clarotes

Common fishes of the Tana River.

and the major food sources for fish are floating material washed down from upstream, and the fruits which tumble into the water from overhanging trees. With their long sensory tentacles the catfish species can locate this sort of food material as it lies on the sandy or muddy bottom. All together the fish party recorded up to seven species of these bottom-feeding fish, each of which was quite distinctive and clearly playing a quite different ecological role below the surface.

The larger species was *Clarotes laticeps*, which remained in the deeper waters of the mainstream and was only captured when our fishermen invented 'Nessy'. This was a large board with steering vanes and an attached line of hooks which would float to the middle of the river when launched and stay there, firmly anchored in the current. In the stiller waters large numbers of the similarly barbelled *Eutropius depressirostris* (meaning flat-mouthed) were recovered, a fish that possesses a long ventral fin but lacks a major fin above. This catfish proved to be no average scavenger, for when it was kept in a tank we found that it would swallow other small fish whole, in some cases taking on a fish that was so large that it would choke on its prey and the fish would die together. Surprisingly, we failed to find the commonest East Africa catfish, *Clarias gariepinus*. This is an interesting species because it is capable of gulping air into its mouth at the water surface and then forcing it backwards into the back of the gill chamber, where a non-collapsible respiratory tree, or modified gill, absorbs oxygen. The absence of this fish was probably due to the fact that we were fishing in fairly well-oxygenated waters and it is probable that it is present in backwaters and meanders.

The other major group of catfish were the *Synodontis* species, odd-looking creatures with bodies that are triangular in section. Their heads and shoulders are heavily armoured, their mouth feelers finely divided to increase their area of sensitivity, while the mouth itself is sucker-like, allowing them to scavenge on the bottom. Like so many of their distant, bottom-feeding relatives, these creatures also possessed sharp spines in front of their erect dorsal fins and alongside the pectoral fins – these sharp anti-predator devices were covered with a slime which caused intense pain when the unwary fisherman was punctured by them. Finally, we also found the fascinating little sucker-mouthed *Chiloglanis brevibarbis*, a diminutive creature which attaches itself to rocks in the falls and feeds on the plant material that grows there in profusion. Thus even though there were many species broadly called catfish, they were obviously clearly separated by their habitat requirements.

In these misty waters we were not surprised, but none the less thrilled to find the elephant-snout fish, a group of fish which lives in muddy conditions and feeds on small creatures located on and below the bottom. The species included the round-headed and bright silver *Petrocephalus catastoma*, the blunt-headed *Gnathocnemus macrolepidotus*, whose lower lip is extended into a short beak, and the truly named elephant-snout fish, *Mormyrus kannume*. These unusual African species possess the remarkable ability to find their way around in these turbid waters by means of an electric current which they generate from two elongated glands either side of the body, just in front of the tail. The glands produce electrical pulses that vary in frequency in response to obstructions. These pulses are recorded by special sensory cells so that the fish find their way around in a manner very much akin to a bat flitting around over the same river in the night sky. In fact, the parallel is very close, for when the fish approaches an obstruction the impulse frequency immediately increases, just like a bat's sonar.

Two other common species in open water were the bright silver *Barbus sp.* and *Labeo sp.* which leapt in the nets like animated quicksilver, their large scaly bodies twinkling as they caught the sun's harsh rays. These creatures are the group that may well have been most affected by the construction of the dams for they are what biologists call anadromous species, or fish which swim up into small permanent tributaries to lay their eggs. These spawning grounds have been isolated upstream of the dams which do not have fish-ladders incorporated into their design. Indeed, although we did not find positive evidence one way or the other, the apparent absence of the large *Barbus mariae* may indicate that it is already extinct. It is also these fish, and especially the *Labeo sp.*, which follow the hippos around waiting for them to disgorge great masses of dung like some gigantic mobile fast-food dispenser, when the fish will dart in and catch any fruits and other tasty morsels before they settle on the bottom. With the two or three *Barbus sp.* we also found the equally brilliant silver carnivore, *Alestes affinis*, whose upward-sloping lower jaw describes its habits, while among the same catches we found rather small numbers of the top minnows *Engraulicypris sp.*, which linger just below the surface. Here they catch small floating food items with their upward-turned mouths.

If there is one African fish that is now famous throughout the tropics because of its amazing social behaviour, it is the *Tilapia*, or *Sarotherodon* as it is now scientifically known. The females incubate the eggs in their mouths, or males and females guard them in pits which they have dug with their mouths on the bottom, and even beyond this phase the young are tended until they are independent. These are the fish that are cultured in fish ponds or form the basis of important lake fisheries, providing the most delectable freshwater fish you could possibly wish to eat. In the Tana we only found small specimens which almost certainly belonged to the species *Sarotherodon spilurus*. Interestingly, we failed to find the Athi or Galana River species *Haplochromis multicolor*, a perfect, twinkling jewel of a fish which was thought to have been introduced into the Tana. This was especially surprising considering the strong geographical affinities between the faunas of these great easterly-flowing rivers.

One of the most interesting discoveries was finding the gobiid fish, *Glossogobius giurus*, which had never been found above Garissa, for the family to which it belongs is that of the big-headed gobies which are commonly found in marine environments such as coral reefs, lagoons and the rock pools of temperate shores. No doubt at some time in the distant past when the Tana began its flow eastwards, this was one of the species which succeeded in colonizing this freshwater environment from the sea. A similar argument must apply to the eels in the river which must also come from the Indian Ocean. Until Peter Whitehead's collections below Garissa in the early 1950s, the young eels or elvers had never been recorded in these waters, so we were pleased to find a further specimen upstream at Kora in 1983. Three species of eels are said to occur in the Tana, and they are said to migrate upstream in June–July, an opinion that was compatible with the fact that our fish party caught several specimens in late July to early August, one of which was a superb mature specimen, nearly a metre (3 ft) long.

To a large degree the Tana seems to have preserved its fauna except for the possibility that some species have been affected by the disruption of upstream migration routes. However, future developments could have a far more serious effect for the projected dams will cut off several permanent rivers from the sea and will further restrict fish movements. To date the only notable introduction in these waters is that of the common guppy, which has no doubt entered the river from nearby waters where it has been maintained for mosquito control, and which now persists in the stiller pools and backwaters. It is also thought that the Asian carp may have escaped into the Tana from fish ponds at Sagana in the highlands during a period of flood. This species has not yet been found downstream of the dams but its potential effects are unpredictable and possibly even catastrophic.

Thus, over a period of about six weeks of active collecting, the fish party added hugely to our knowledge of the Tana's fish fauna, and above all contributed the sort of vital base-line data which will allow future biologists to measure changes in the face of further development, such as increases in the silt burden and in the level of water conductivity as a result of erosion generated by subsistence agriculture upstream.

them, they must have a function which is of value to the tree. In the case of the *Commiphora*, there seemed little doubt that the primary function of the resin was to heal wounds, for where the bark or branches had been damaged by large mammals or some other agency, the resin had quickly oozed out to cover the damage. This would prevent the entry of insects and fungi which are always at hand to invade the interior of a damaged plant, even in this hostile landscape. Additionally, though, the quite high resin pressures produced within the plant must also act as a great deterrent to chewing insects. If it were not for the fact that they would be faced with a flood of resin that would be distasteful and may be poisonous, such insects would attack and defoliate these plants during their period of greatest abundance in the rains. It must surely be no coincidence that Man has used resins as fumigants for several thousand years. How plants came to produce resins is a more difficult question, but the selective forces that must have led to their evolution do not now seem to be associated, as was formerly believed, with the development of accidental by-products of normal metabolism, but rather, in many cases, the substances do seem to have evolved because of their special function in deterring attack by herbivorous predators.

The family Burseraceae, to which the myrrh belongs, all contain resins and are distributed in Central and South America, Africa, Asia and northern Australia. *Commiphora* and its close relative *Boswellia* (frankincense) seem to have originated in eastern Africa, in the Somali region and down through that long tongue of arid country that includes the Kora National Reserve. Commercial use of the gum resin of myrrh (which contains between 25 to 40 per cent resin and 2 to 8 per cent of the oil myrrhol, the main agent of scent) is based on many different substances which are derived from the species that occur in Africa, Arabia and India, and which are still gathered and exported from many of these areas, although surprisingly they are of little commercial importance in Kenya. Indeed Peter was included in our survey team to look for potential uses for the indigenous resins in the fields of perfumery, medicine and other chemical processes in order that their commercial value might be exploited to provide a source of income for the inhabitants of the more arid regions of eastern Africa. Peter's work was unfortunately misunderstood by some people who had visions of resin collectors wandering over Kora slashing trees, though of course there had never been any intention to focus exploitation on the Reserve. On the other hand, considering the extent to which these sensitive woodlands are lopped for feed for domestic animals and felled for building poles or the production of charcoal, it is clear that, if resin collection were commercially viable, it could prove to be an important means of reducing if not preventing the removal of trees and the destruction of these sensitive arid habitats that are so prone to erosion.

Initially we were surprised and heartened by the large number of *Commiphora* species that occurred in Kora. Individual species are in fact very difficult to identify, so Peter gave them numbers based upon their physiognomic characteristics, such as their shape, the nature of their spines and bark, and the colour of the underbark when slashed, as well as their resins. This proved to be a surprisingly useful means of identification for the *Commiphora* varied from low scrubby species to tall, almost majestic trees. Using Peter's system it was quite easy, even for the non-botanist, to distinguish the main species. *Commiphora* usually has a pale grey, pale green or blue bark that is often flaky or powdery in texture. The branches, which may be smooth or densely covered in spines, grow in a great aerial tangle at the end of a short trunk. This twisted mass forms a fairly impenetrable barrier to Man, but is a haven for birds and a wide variety of other animals. By the end of the study the botanists had found thirteen suspected species of *Commiphora* which were identified on the basis of the following characteristics.

The first identifying feature was whether the branchlets oozed resin when they were bent, and species falling into this category included *Commiphora rostrata*, *C. erosa* and *C. erythraea*. The *Commiphora rostrata* was soon well known to all our workers for although it was an insignificant low tree, seldom more than a metre or so high, when the branches were bent either accidentally or deliberately its fluid resin would run down the stem and often squirted a considerable distance as a fine, vaporized mist. As soon as this happened the air was immediately filled with an acrid cat-like odour that quickly earned it the name of 'cat's pee tree'. Its odour was also reminiscent of kerosene, an association which turned out to be correct when our knowledgeable APU friends and protectors showed us that a piece of string soaked in the resin would burn readily with a smoky flame. Other identifying features were the colour of the trunk when slashed, the quantity of resin produced and resin hardness, while some species were classified on the basis of their bark, spines or mode of branching.

In the early travels into the bush and during later discussions in the Herbarium, the botanists were able to distinguish a further nine or ten species on this basis. Interestingly, the character of the trees' resins enabled the Herbarium botanists to at least provisionally separate species that they had found it impossible to distinguish on the basis of their flower and leaf characteristics. At the final count we had confirmed the presence of *Commiphora africana* (of which perhaps two distinct forms occur), *C. boiviniana*, *C. campestris* (three possible forms, one of which is the magnificent flat-topped umbrella type with a knobbed trunk that has a restricted distribution in the southwest of the Reserve), *C. engleri*, *C. incisa*, *C. longipedicellata* and *C. mollis*. Such long lists of scientific names are somewhat off-putting to the non-specialist, but these are the names by which these plants can be recognized throughout the world, irrespective of the local language. In the case of Kenya, for example, *Commiphora africana* is known by various tribal names – dabba un un, ekedille, amess or mbambara.

Alongside the myrrh trees were small scrubby specimens of *Boswellia neglecta*, whose stature hardly seemed to mark them out as the source of the historic frankincense (olibanum), or ubani as it is known in Hindi, Arabic and Swahili. Different species of *Boswellia* produce resins with slightly different odours but they are all used as aromatics, as they have been since Pliny described them as *spuma pingius*. Up to 70 per cent of this resin is soluble in alcohol, but a large proportion is also soluble in water, producing a substance that is very similar to gum arabic – an acacia gum. Its aromatic oil is referred to as oliben, a name whose origin must be close to the 'liban', or 'luban', of the Arab world and which is still used in Swahili for a *Commiphora* species which has an almost identical odour to frankincense.

As we helped Peter with his collecting, our association with the APU proved invaluable for they described the wide variety of uses to which their various peoples put these resins today, and it was a formidable list. They are variously employed as antiseptics (a use confirmed on our own cuts), incense, for repairing holes in car radiators, and as a chewing gum which retains its resinous flavour for a considerable period and was soon being munched by most of our party.

In all, the various species of *Commiphora* were found to contribute up to 70 per cent of the tree cover of the Kora bush, a fact confirmed by the view from the summit of a rock outcrop which showed these pale grey or blue-green trees with their twisted branches spread out over the landscape like a giant spider's web. Interspersed with the *Commiphora*, however, were the acacia trees with their invariably white spines giving them an almost misty appearance as they stretched their spiny fingers to the sky. To most visitors, or the compulsive viewer of television wildlife films, the flat-topped acacia is a veritable symbol of Africa, providing the background against which giraffes stroll across the skyline, or under which elephants stand quietly during the heat of the day, gently flapping their ears in an effort to keep cool. Like so many other living organisms the acacias play an important role in the ecology of the bush and are inextricably interwoven with the lives of a whole host of other animals and plants.

The acacia belongs to the mimosa family and is widespread throughout Central and South America, Africa, India, southeast Asia and Australia. In all there are up to 900 species, but half of these are found only in Australia. Recent chemical studies of the seeds of these Australian species suggest that their separation from species in the rest of the world dates back to the break-up of the great Gondwanaland continent about 75 million years ago, the time when the present-day continents separated from each other. Up to 42 species are recorded in Kenya, of which we were to find 13 in the tiny wilderness of Kora. Some of these were species that are widespread over most of Africa, Arabia and western India, while others had an amazingly restricted distribution in the Horn of Africa, or even a disjunct distribution in Somalia and southwest Africa, indicating yet again that a corridor of dry country must have connected these two extreme corners of the vast continent at some period in the distant past.

The East African acacias vary from low thorny bushes to large trees and their distribution ranges from semi-desert regions to the montane forests of the Kenya highlands. Except for the riverine and highland species, most of these acacias are deciduous and lose their foliage in the dry season. The leaves vary from species to species, some having a single pair of leaflets, others a leaf arrangement which botanists call bipinnate. In the latter a series of stalks (pinnae) are arranged along the side of the main leaf stalk and each of these bears a row of tiny paired leaflets. This pattern of bearing tiny leaflets on a single leaf has been variously seen as an adaptation to reduce water loss or wind damage, but it seemed to us that the main function was to deter predators. It was apparent that it was much more difficult for a caterpillar or other herbivorous insect to feed on these easily detached units than on larger undivided leaves.

At the beginning of the rains these trees develop their main leaf cover very rapidly and this is closely followed by a vast mass of blossoms, each of which consists of a densely packed group of tiny tubular flowers. These are arranged either in a compact pompom typical of the mimosa, or as an elongated spike which may vary in colour from white, cream or pink to brilliant yellow. Each tiny flower is a brush of male anthers producing liberal quantities of pollen, a major attraction for a multitude of bees which fill the air with a loud and continuous orchestral hum. The flowers also attract brilliantly coloured sunbirds seeking nectar, and insectivorous birds hunting the wide variety of insects that have gathered to share the nutritious and sugary feast.

The most characteristic feature of these trees is the armoury of spines and thorns which lines the branches, providing a virtually impenetrable barrier to large mammals, including Man. For smaller creatures such as birds and rodents, however, the harsh canopies offer considerable protection. A bird known as the white-headed buffalo weaver goes so far as to reinforce this protection by collecting spiny twigs and arranging them along the branches leading to its nest, in what is believed to be an attempt to deter attack by arboreal snakes. In general, the thorns arise in pairs or threes below the leaves, but there are a small number of species that have thorns scattered all over their stems like a briar. In examining the species that occurred in Kora I quickly discovered that we could distinguish them even when they were not in flower or fruit by their vegetative characteristics, such as their spines, hooks or bark. For example, some species bear pairs of small or large spines, others pairs of sharply curved hooks or thorns, while another group has hooks arranged in threes, an outer pair bending upwards and a central one downwards. Finally, there is one species that takes every precaution and has spines and hooks, arranged either in pairs of spines or hooks, or in a pair consisting of a spine and a hook. These acacia species closely resembled vegetable pin-cushions and it was easy to imagine that they had evolved as adaptations to prevent feeding by large herbivores. This proved not to be the case, however, for we only had to watch a giraffe, a lesser kudu, or a gerenuk to realize that they were very adept at moving their delicate mouths along the branches to remove the shoots and leaves, or simply at stripping them with their tongues, moving in the same direction as the forward-pointing spines. Indeed a Cambridge biologist has recently suggested that the spines do not stop mammals feeding, but rather

The next day we set out with Eregumsa and two of his Korakora (Oroma) friends, a vehicle full of pangas (long, sharp, machette-like knives which are used for everything from cutting wood and opening coconuts to weeding a farm plot or planting trees), and a multitude of helpers. Andrew left camp ready for anything in a smart new blue safari jacket and a blue hat, with a compass, a hand lens, a water bottle and a camera slung around his neck on a series of cords that threatened to strangle him at any moment. I had ensured that we had loaded the most important equipment of all, several large Thermos flasks full of Meilo's good strong tea that would sustain us in the heat until we returned in the early afternoon. Dear Andrew could never understand our working habits, for he felt that we should suffer the blistering sun from dawn till dusk.

For our first transect half a kilometre (550 yd) downstream of base camp, we cut a line from the river bank that passed through the riverine bush before entering the *Acacia-Commiphora* to the south of the main track. Eregumsa's two fellow Korakora tribesmen, Ramadani and Dero, were experts at bush cutting for they had been part of Terence Adamson's road gang when the Kora road system was cut. Together with the botanists they began clearing the *Salvadora* bush which rose from the sandy riverine soil like a badly-tangled vegetable wig, disturbing as they went tiny bush squirrels, and crested francolins that cackled in protest. On the river a boat party set out to the transect base to measure the profile of the river bottom. This would provide a valuable starting point for the aquatic biologists and the entomologists who had already started to place pitfall traps across the sandy bank.

An essential piece of equipment for the transect cutters was the hoko, a stout stick about 2 m (6 ft) long, which bore a fork at one end and a hook at the other. This simple piece of local woodwork was carried by all the Somali and Korakora people, especially when they were faced with bush in which *Acacia senegal* was a common constituent. These trees bore a set of three hooks below each leaf axil, and since their branches arched outwards and then hung downwards, the net result was to produce a vicious wall that defied penetration – hence their more common name 'wait-a-bit', or 'ngoja kidogo' in Swahili. According to Terence Adamson, these trees have become much more common and larger in recent years because poaching has drastically reduced the numbers of black rhino. These animals browse heavily on the young plants and so the decline in their numbers has led to the establishment of a dense thicket, creating a veritable 'no-go area' over much of the Reserve. The hoko was very useful for cutting a track through this bush for if the thorny branches were pushed away with the fork, the base of the tree or bush could be easily severed with a panga, and the branches then pulled clear with the wooden hook on the other end of the hoko.

Along the edge of the water stout tufts of handsome sedge – *Cyperus articulatus* – sprouted alongside the greeny-white flowered milkweed – *Kanahia lanifolia*. Above them the delicate pink flowers of the liberally hooked scrambler *Caesalpinia trothea* shone brightly against the dark green background, until they were eaten by a group of white-bellied turacos which climbed amongst the branches wagging their tall head crests as they went about their noisy business. At the top of the river bank the henna bushes were loaded with fruit and flowers, a source of food for the fruit-eating birds, while their lower branches were neatly trimmed in a straight line by Basil and his relatives. The famous red dye obtained from the henna (*Lawsonia inermis*) is extracted by crushing the leaves and then adding lemon juice to the expressed fluid before applying it to the hair, beard, hands or feet, in time-honoured Muslim fashion. Oddly enough, this material suddenly seems to have become common in the West, where there is now hardly a shampoo or hair conditioner that does not boast henna as a vital constituent. Even in Kora a young lady who had come to help George was most upset when Peter failed to tell her how to extract the magic ingredient, though I still wonder if she ever followed our suggestion that she should wash her hair in henna juice and then rinse it liberally in lemon juice, which should have produced the suitably brilliant and unexpected scarlet of a haji fresh back from Mecca.

The narrow strip of riverine trees included the doum palm, distinguished by the fact that it is one of only two palms to have branching stems (the other is the Nipa palm of the Far East). These stems are individually crowned by spirals of large fan-shaped leaves, many of which now graced the roofs of our buildings. This riverine strip also included the graceful flat-topped *Acacia tortilis*, and the thicker-trunked *Acacia elatior*, whose outer branches were arched outwards and gracefully downwards. Tamarinds grew right at the edge of the river, with drooping pinnate leaves and a fruit from which cool drinks, chutneys and medicines are made, and which is also an obligatory component of all good curries. The Tana River poplar (*Populus ilicifolia*) was also one of the commoner fringing trees. This is the furthest-south member of the poplar family, and in Kenya is found only along the Tana, Athi and Uaso Nyiro river systems, where its coarse, dark brown timber is much sought after for making dug-out canoes.

Each transect was cut approximately at right angles to the river, track or other starting point, and the line of the strip was marked by red-topped poles

ABOVE RIGHT In the point centre quarter method of assessing tree cover, the distance to the nearest tree trunk is measured at each sampling point and the tree species recorded. Four measurements are taken at each point, one for each quadrant.

BELOW RIGHT The bitterlich stick method of assessing tree cover assumes that trees have cylindrical trunks and that they will appear in plan as a scatter of circles on the ground. The further away they are, the smaller they appear from a fixed point, and the apparent diameter of any one has a direct relationship with the proportion of ground plan area it occupies. Using a simple cross bar, held an exact distance from the eye, boles that appear larger than the bar are counted while those that are not are ignored. Altering the distance of the cross bar from the eye changes the trunk size that the stick will record. In Kora the bar was set so that one tree exceeding its width at any sample point meant that 1 per cent of the ground area around the observer was covered by tree trunks. This figure is, of course, highly notional, but it does make it possible to compare woodlands and tree species, as well as to get some idea of the volume of wood available.

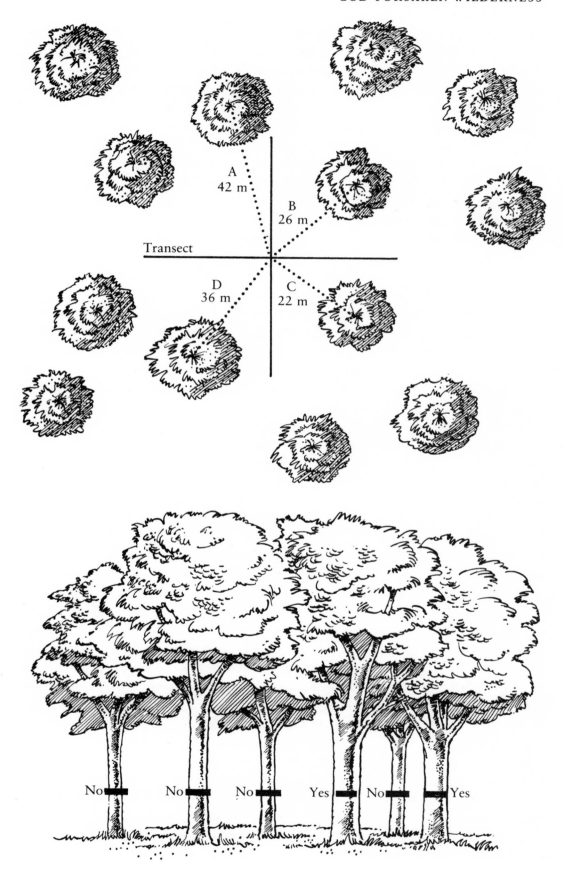

A
42 m

B
26 m

Transect

D
36 m

C
22 m

No   No   No   Yes   No   Yes

coming to Kora he had already examined the aerial photographs, and using these together with the preliminary information that KREMU had collected on the ground in their excursions with our team allowed them to draw a simple vegetation map on which they could site their sampling stations. They chose eight ground stations in all, which they set out to sample with amazing speed. Excluding the riverine vegetation, they identified five major bush types within the complex *Acacia-Commiphora* mosaic, which they designated:

1 *Bushed shrubland* This type was largely located in the southern end of the Reserve and had a crown cover of about 51 per cent, and a tree density of about 470 trees per hectare (2½ acres), as Andrew and his party had already observed. Up to half this cover was contributed by the handsome spreading-branched *Commiphora erythraea*. The rest of the cover was dominated by the seasonal shrubs *Bauhinia taitensis*, *Boscia coriacea*, *Grewia villosa*, and the devilish *Acacia senegal*. The herb layer was rich in perennial grasses with many species together contributing a ground cover of 18 per cent, and the forbs or weeds another 5 per cent.

2 *Shrubland* This type was located mainly in the central and eastern parts of the Reserve where it extended over a very wide area in conditions of fairly widespread soil erosion. The bush was rich in tree species with a density of 813 per hectare, and a rich shrub understory in which the widespread *Bauhinia* contributed a quarter of the cover. While the ground cover of 25 per cent was mainly made up of perennial grasses, the grass cover had been almost completely removed on the Reserve's eastern boundary where the influence of Somali domestic stock was the greatest.

3 *Shrubland thicket* This type of vegetation was mainly found on the pediment platforms around the Kiume outcrop and between the Mbubu and Chanyigi sand rivers, where plant density averaged 2400 per hectare. Here again the shrubby *Bauhinia* was prominent, contributing nearly half of the plants counted, although the desert canopy cover was provided by acacia and *Commiphora*. The addition of *Cordia abyssinica*, *Sericocomopsis* (a common low shrub of open, often disturbed grasslands), and *Loewia tanaensis* gave this shrubland a character of its own. In the central parts of the Reserve the vegetation did not show signs of being affected by domestic stock, and the dead plant litter on the surface was fairly abundant, but in the east the pressure was clearly high. The herbaceous ground cover was 14 per cent with a rich grass and forb flora.

4 *Wooded shrubland* This type of vegetation was found in three distinct areas, with one patch in the west of the Reserve, one inland from the Tana River west of base camp, and a third in the vicinity of the Kora ridge. It was dominated by acacia and *Commiphora* which together with the other component species produced a distinguishing high canopy cover of 82 per cent and a tree density of 1484 per hectare. Not surprisingly, the grass and herb cover was a low 9 per cent because of the dense trees.

5 *Bushland thicket* This habitat covered a wide area in the west of the Reserve, but showed a decreasing tree cover which fell from 1486 per hectare near the Tana to 1024 per hectare 20 km (12 miles) further south. *Commiphora campestris* dominated the cover throughout the area. Interestingly, the decreasing tree cover was accompanied by an increasing woody plant cover which rose from 63 per cent near the river to 93 per cent further south. In areas cut by luggas the riverine vegetation extended its range inland. The herb cover also rose from 11 per cent near the Tana to 18 per cent in the south, with a probable increase in the diversity of grass species.

Clearly a division into vegetation groups of this kind is not very exact in such a complex mosaic, but it did allow the sort of classification that could be used to advantage by the other study groups. Moses' merry band of workers visited the eight sites and carried out 'point centre quarter' and 'bitterlich stick' measurements as Andrew's group had. In addition they established a baseline in each sampling area and placed a transect at right angles to it along which they marked out quadrants (square plots). They then clipped the herb vegetation on these plots and estimated the plant cover and the weight of each species. These estimates were carried out in August 1983 and then again in March 1984, a period during which the 'short rains' failed completely and nearly 50 per cent of the herb cover disappeared across all the sample plots. Across the five vegetation types the standing crop biomass (the actual weight of vegetation found above ground) varied from 301 kg (662 lb) per hectare in bushland thicket to 602 kg (1324 lb) per hectare in wooded shrubland, while tree density reached its lowest level of 473 trees per hectare in bushed shrubland and an astonishing figure of 2400 trees per hectare (five times larger) in shrubland thicket.

Organization is of the essence in this sort of country, for the longer the work takes the greater the expense in terms of the cost of petrol, vehicle maintenance and rations. Moses and his team carried out their work with great speed and efficiency and then they all departed down the Mwingi road to Nairobi to the metaphorical strains of that great old East African army song 'Funga Safari', which can be literally translated as 'the safari is ended, we are on our way home'. Shortly after they left they were followed by the main botanical survey party. Although the botanists felt that what they had been doing would never really be finished, they had at least produced an indication of how the vegetation was composed and could leave the production of further plant species records to the Herbarium team, who still sat and hoped that it would rain sometime. The KREMU team also wait for some rain so that they can revisit their ground stations before they attempt to interpret their own observations in conjunction with those of Andrew Agnew's group.

— 5 —
Islands in the Bush

From the very first of our visits to Kora the rock outcrops or inselbergs held a particular fascination, for from their invariably bare summits we could watch the sun rise or set, and be bathed in a cool breeze that seldom penetrated the dense bush below. Whenever I asked Nigel what he would like to do when he managed to get away from Nairobi for a short break his reply was nearly always 'Let's see the sunrise from Kiume'. At 5.30 am we would crawl from our beds and drive slowly away from the sleeping camp, making our way over the Monune lugga where we often met George's lions at the river's edge, and then on up to the base of the outcrop. Here we would climb to its rounded peak, sit in virtual silence and watch the sun creep over the eastern horizon, first as a bright orange wash on the low-lying misty clouds, and then as a brilliant golden orb that seemed to rush skyward as if it were being pushed by an unseen celestial hand. Indeed, as we sat there it was not difficult to imagine how early human groups must have felt it natural to worship the coming and going of this daily source of heat and life. Before long, however, the sun's rays would begin to burn into our bare chests, making us realize that the equatorial sun is a mixed blessing. The sun gives life, but in the harsh drought that was gripping Kora the heat was evaporating what little water there still was in the parched earth, upon which only 10 cm (4 in) of rain had fallen in the previous eighteen months. From the top of the outcrop we could see the Tana River winding from the western to the eastern horizon, like a brown ribbon neatly edged with green, and hear the land waking up as the birds began to call in the bush below.

Dotted in an apparently random jumble across the Kora landscape other rock outcrops rose in sharp relief to the dark greys and dull greens of the bush. The Kiume outcrop that we sat on was one of a group of hills clustered together on a rocky platform, while to the east we could see a whole line of hills with Kora standing out sharply in the centre. To our south there were several small, elongated ridges, rocky and knife-edged, and beyond them the well vegetated slopes and the flat top of Nzoka (meaning snake in Wakamba,

FAR LEFT *A male gerenuk stretches its elegant neck, head and lyre-shaped horns to sample a succulent morsel on the tip of a bush. In taller vegetation it will stand on its hind legs to feed.*

LEFT *The most common hoofed mammal of Kora is the tiny dik-dik, which lives in small family groups in a close and long-term bond between the male and female. Here the horned male is in the foreground and the hornless female in the background.*

BELOW *The majestic African elephant is a transient inhabitant of the Reserve. These animals can reach the tips of most trees with their trunks, and if necessary will use their massive strength to push the tree over.*

OVERLEAF *Two Masai giraffe peer under a large acacia tree at intruders. With the exception of the elephant, the giraffe can reach higher than any other herbivore to browse on the rich sources of food in the trees' canopies. Browsing often alters the shape of the canopies.*

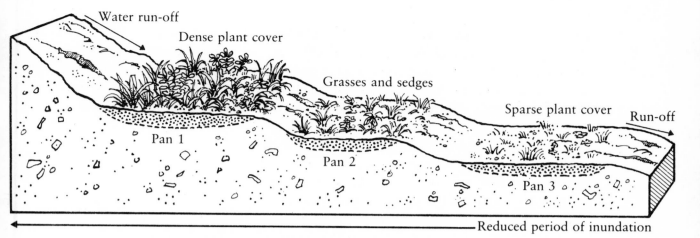

Water run-off

Dense plant cover

Grasses and sedges

Sparse plant cover

Run-off

Pan 1

Pan 2

Pan 3

Reduced period of inundation

Rock pans develop as saucer-shaped solution cavities where the surface of an outcrop is more or less flat. On sloping ground, they will often develop along lines of weakness in the rock so that the surface shows a sequence of such pans. As a result of water percolating down from soil and vegetation, pans at the bottom of the sequence will often be flooded for several weeks while those at the top are only transiently wet. These differences are reflected in changes in vegetation and associated fauna down the slope.

that you could forget to water. The aptly named *Xerophyta* consisted of bunches of dark woody stems up to 30 cm (1 ft) tall with tightly rolled, spike-like leaves rising from them. When wetted the leaves unrolled from their bases, quickly turned green and resumed growth almost immediately, producing pale-violet sweetly-scented flowers from between the leaf bases several days later, no doubt as an attraction to some discerning insect.

Animal life also had this ability to withstand drying out, usually surviving the dry season as eggs in the dusty soil at the bottom of the rock pools. In most cases these pans would only contain water for short periods, but if they were one of a series arranged down a slope they could be fed for some time after it had rained with a slow trickle of water draining from the soils that were trapped higher up the outcrop. In some cases the water flow was channelled into cracks from which the softer material had been eroded. The commonest organisms to be found in such ephemeral pools were the crustaceans. These are invertebrates with external skeletons (arthropods) belonging to the same group as the woodlouse, lobster and crab. Almost anywhere in the arid tropics temporary pools are filled with 'fairy shrimps' after a few days of rain – pale, transparent-bodied, elongated creatures belonging to the genus *Streptocephalus*, which swim on their backs and filter food from the water with a row of paired limbs that are fringed with stiff hairs acting as sieves. The Kora shrimps were a surprise to me for they were nearly 2 cm (1 in) long and had bright red tails, exactly the same as creatures I had seen in village ponds in southern India at the beginning of the monsoon. The most remarkable feature of these animals is that they hatch from their dried eggs in the pool bottoms within hours of rain having fallen, and then grow on to maturity and reproduce within ten days, small black eggs accumulating in a narrow egg-sack hanging down between their legs. This life cycle is only possible because the warm water is a nutrient soup, rich in all sorts of organic material such as the dried dung of lizards and other creatures. In these conditions bacteria, algae and single-celled animals multiply rapidly, producing a steady supply of food for the fairy shrimps which lazily buzz along on their backs, kicking it into their mouths with their feet. What a life!

After *Streptocephalus* has passed through its life history and died, it is often replaced by several other crustaceans, especially the ostracods which buzz around the surface of the water like animated ball bearings, their outer bodies covered by a two-valved globular shell. They beat their fringed legs inside the shell to draw in water from which they filter out food particles in the same way as the fairy shrimps. In some of the larger pools, there was more than one species of these creatures, often accompanied by the very common *Daphnia* of our temperate ponds. These are built in much the same way as the ostracods with lateral shields that enable them to direct a water current over and between their hair-fringed limbs which act as filters for food particles. Many of the Kora pool dwellers are as yet unnamed but their presence is often evident, even in the dry season. The large blue patches that we saw in the centre of the bigger pools were formed partly of the skeletons of the bright blue ostracods and partly of their eggs which awaited the return of the rains.

Probably the most remarkable of all the creatures that inhabit these rock pools in Kenya and Uganda (although it has not yet been found in Kora) is a minute midge (a two-winged fly), which glorifies in the very grand name of *Polypedilum vanderplanki*. This insect, like its cousins the gnats and mosquitos, goes through its life history quite rapidly in seasonal pools, where its typical elongated larva feeds with special mouth brush filters and breathes through siphons at the water surface. There is of course nothing odd about these habits, but if the pool evaporates before the larvae pupate, they are capable of losing over 80 per cent of their body water, dehydrating to such an extent that you could crumble them to dust between your fingers. Yet when the rains return and they are rewetted they will rehydrate within the space of an hour, resume feeding, pupate and emerge as adults to start a new insect generation in a matter of days.

What is odd about this midge is that it resists the dry season as a larva, for it is much more common, even normal, for insects and other forms of life to pass this difficult season as an egg. One of the most extreme adaptations is the life cycle of a small group of fish belonging to the guppy family, which pass through their whole life history in a few weeks and survive the dry season as dried eggs in the bottom of pools or seasonal streams. One of these species is the East African *Notobranchius guentheri*, a brilliantly coloured fish much in demand for aquariums, which has been introduced to many other tropical areas as a means of mosquito control because of its remarkable ability to survive aridity. In the case of this and similar species natural selection has produced an 'annual fish' which cannot breed successfully in permanent water, for its eggs will not hatch unless they are dried out.

The predominantly quartz-gravel soil of the outcrops is not suitable for burrowing animals, but the perched boulders and rock debris make an ideal environment that many creatures have succeeded in colonizing. If you look at the jumbled rock masses from a distance you will invariably see bright white patches on the rock faces, a hard, white, shiny coating which will extend downwards from a ledge. When we clambered up onto the rocks, we soon saw piles of almost round pellets and the air was filled with a strong nitrogenous odour. In places the piles were over 30 cm (1 ft) deep, indicating that the creature that produced them must have been using the site as a midden, perhaps in order to advertise its presence and demarcate its territory by visual and olfactory means. Had I not been very familiar with this creature, I might have gone on wondering what kind of animal was responsible for the dung and the long white urine marks on the rock face, for nothing moved and not a creature showed itself. I knew, however, that if we had been there in the early morning we would have spotted groups of tailless mammals about the size of a rabbit with rounded backs and blunt heads perched high on the rock facing the morning sun. Occasionally the males would open their mouths and emit a high-pitched wail, and at our approach would disappear with alarm calls and a harsh bark. These odd-looking creatures are the hyraxes, or the biblical coney, found throughout the African continent from Syria to South Africa but nowhere else.

Today we only have three genera of hyrax, two of the social rock hyrax and one that is a solitary tree dweller of the dense rain and montane forests. Small though the hyraxes are, they are descended from creatures that were the size of bears in the Miocene period. Some features of their anatomy, including a pair of sharp tusks in the upper jaw, indicate that they have evolved from the group of primitive ungulates that also gave rise to the elephants and sea-cows. Other features are peculiar to the hyrax alone and these include divided incisor teeth in the lower jaw for fur combing, and a curved nail on the inner toe of the hind foot that is used for the same purpose. The toes terminate in neat little nails that are very reminiscent of those found on the foot of an elephant and a particularly mobile pelvis is an aid to their spectacular jumping skills, which can lift them 2 m (6 ft) into the air from a standing position. But perhaps the most remarkable feature of the hyrax is its 7.3-month gestation period, incredibly long for such a small creature and another indication that it has its origins in much larger creatures that existed twenty or so million years ago.

Like many of the smaller African creatures, the hyraxes have been endowed with mysterious properties and woven into tribal legends. The hyrax appears to be able to stare into the sun and this led people to presume that they are blind, for how else, they argue, would it be possible to stare into this golden light and still be able to see? On moonlit nights the plaintive wails of the rock hyraxes echo in the silence and few tribesmen will venture near them in the eery light for the child-like sounds are said to be the voices of long-dead children. The deafening cry of the solitary tree hyrax is even more eery, starting

ISLANDS IN THE BUSH

with a wail and ending in a strangled scream that makes the hair on the back of your head stand on end, even when you know what is making the noise. The beliefs about the hyrax date back a very long way, while its dried urine was an item of trade in the ancient world. Known as 'Hyraceum', it followed the same route north as the myrrh, frankincense and henna. Today the urine is still used in folk medicine to cure kidney and bladder complaints, and even to soothe hysteria, and our APU men were not slow in collecting it from the outcrops.

The Kora hyrax occur as two quite different forms, one being the rather chunky *Procavia johnstoni*, and the other the smaller and paler *Heterohyrax brucei*. Both live in social groups on the outcrops but usually only the latter species is found on the small outcrops, both species occurring together on the larger rock masses such as Katania, where the number of cavities is far more numerous and the holes themselves larger. These two forms of hyrax look alike but they are clearly quite separate reproductively for, although they live together, they do not interbreed and hybrids are unknown. In the weeks we scrambled over the outcrops, many of these quaint little mammals became very tame and watched our clumsy antics with apparent amusement. The hyrax is well known for the fact that it can be tamed very quickly and these animals can become charming pets, living quite freely in the house. Since they urinate and defecate over the edges of rocks in the wild, they will soon learn to use a sink or even the lavatory. Indeed Richard Leakey's father, a great hyrax fan, used to say 'the only thing you cannot teach a hyrax to do is to pull the chain'. For us Kora seemed a natural place to watch hyrax for one of the famous Adamson animals was Pati-Pati, the animal that appeared as the whisky-drinking rock hyrax in the book *Born Free* and subsequently in the film.

Clearly any animal that can tolerate the very dry conditions of Kora must be specially adapted, an evolutionary feature that is reflected in the fact that the hyrax has nearly solid urine and dry dung from which virtually all the vital life-giving water has been removed. But perhaps the most striking of this mammal's adaptations is its body temperature which varies with the environment, rising when the air is hot and falling at night. This characteristic is more reminiscent of a lizard than a mammal, but the temperature range of the hyrax is much less than in a cold-blooded vertebrate like a lizard. The ability to alter body temperature plays an essential role in water conservation, for if the temperature can be raised with that of the environment, the water lost in evaporative cooling is much less, a feature well illustrated in the desert-dwelling camel. Moreover, dwelling in the interstices of piles of boulders allows the hyrax to live in very nearly constant conditions. The animal raises its body temperature by basking in the sun every morning and late afternoon so it does not have to use its own metabolic energy to create heat. Having heated itself up in the morning, the hyrax then rests in the constant conditions of its rocky home and digests its food like an animated compost heap. This way of life is assisted by their long rows of molar teeth with which they can gather their day's food in less than an hour. By turning their heads sideways they can cut

in the bottom of sugary teacups. By following these busy little animals to their source we quickly discovered that they came from the end of a broken branch on the big acacia. Where the branch had been fractured three small waxy tubes, like miniature yellow trumpets, emerged from a crack, and busy little insects buzzed in and out at great speed, the miniature pollen baskets on their hind legs indicating that they were bees. These tiny social creatures are only about 3 mm (0.4 in) long, and are commonly called 'sweat bees' because of their annoying habit of gathering around the eyes in tiny swarms, and crawling over people's bodies. They are unusual in that they are one of the few bees that are stingless. They live inside hollow trees where they construct their nests partly from wax which they have produced from special glands, and partly from natural gums and resins which they have gathered from the trees. Using gum, resin and wax, they also make a temporary plug to close the nest at night in order to keep out their enemies. Within the nest they have the same social order as other bees, but the queen is much less easily distinguished from the other inhabitants than is the case with honey bees. These tiny nests contain a sweet dark honey that is much enjoyed by the people of the African bush. Peering inside we saw the tiny brood cells, and the much larger waxy cells that looked like tiny bright-yellow mulberries because of the minute lumps of nectar and pollen that had been deposited in them. Our little colony remained close to our table in spite of their annoying habits and our frequent threats to remove them, for most of us felt that they had been there much longer than us.

Our entomologists travelled extensively with the various groups that visited every corner of the Reserve, but because of the dry conditions the most rewarding spots for finding insects were generally the riverine forest and our base camp. During the heat of the day very little moved unless there was a tree in flower, when butterflies appeared suddenly in large numbers to take advantage of the temporary bounty. After sunset, though, when things were cooler, insects would suddenly appear even in the dry season and fill the night air with their whirring wings before they disappeared again, as suddenly as they had come. Our dining table was never a very formal affair in the evening, especially as Joseph Muhangani, our enthusiastic entomologist from the Museum, would suddenly lean forward over the table to examine some small insect intently before popping it into a tube with a chuckle of evident pleasure. In this way he collected several more interesting specimens for our collection. The one environment close at hand that did not suffer the same seasonality as the dry bush was the strip bordering the river, as the Tana continued to flow on past us in spite of the lack of rain up country. During the day the stiller patches of water close to the shore were populated by rapidly moving groups of whirligig beetles (Gyrinidae), that sped round and round in circles like miniature motorboats. These tiny black insects have dense hairs on their middle and hind legs which enable them to swim about on the surface to catch floating pieces of food. When disturbed they disappear instantly from sight, en masse.

Even on bright sunny days dragonflies would appear and hover motionless over the water looking for prey. When they spotted something they would dart

155

downwards to grasp the unfortunate insect with the long black legs that hung down from their robust thoraxes, and then return to a perch to consume their prey, their jaws working backwards and forwards in a scissor-like motion. The dragonflies came in all colours, from green and scarlet to the superb irridescent blue of the smoky-winged damsel flies that clung to reeds along the shore, or darted down to the surface of still pools to deftly deposit an egg below the surface. These eggs hatched into fearsome-looking predatory larvae which are capable of shooting their jaws out a considerable distance from the underside of their heads to grasp their prey. We commonly associate dragonflies with water and an odd feature of one of the African species is that we would suddenly see them flying in large swarms several kilometres from the river. In the middle of dry acacia bush they would be darting hither and thither and grasping prey from the top of the bushes. This odd phenomenon was proof of the fact that these dull brown dragonflies can migrate considerable distances and were probably *Pantala flavescens*. This species has been observed in vast numbers in the middle of the Pacific Ocean, 1400 km (900 miles) from the coast of Australia, as well as over most of eastern Africa where they suddenly appear and then vanish just as swiftly.

The evenings were, however, the favourite time for insects to arrive in abundance, and the commonest of these nocturnal visitors were the five or six species of mayfly (Ephemeroptera), whose sudden emergence appeared to be related to the phases of the moon. In a few minutes the lamps over our table would pass from a state of insectless peace to one of a thousand fluttering wings. These elegant creatures had long slim abdomens that curved upwards and terminated in three, long, hair-like, sensitive *circae*. Their finely net-veined wings were arranged so that the much smaller hind wings fitted neatly behind a pair of large forewings. They would cling to the lampshade, their delicate wings fluttering, and when they took to the wing the females would be grabbed hastily by the males, for since many species live for less than a day finding a mate is an important and urgent business. This frantic sexual activity was observed closely by our project members, partly for its intrinsic entomological interest, but partly, I suspect, because they had been in the bush a little too long. Another peculiarity of these delicate creatures was the fact that, after they hatched from the water, these apparent adults had to undergo another moult before they reached their true adult stage, a characteristic unique amongst insects. Their aquatic lives are spent as larvae with three slim tails which breathe by means of flat plate-like gills that are arranged in various patterns along their abdomens.

The dry conditions we experienced meant that even when Mark Ritchie, Joseph Muhangani and Mike Clifton set up their nocturnal insect trap, with its brilliant light which could be seen for a long way, very few insects visited it, although those that did often turned out to be particularly interesting. One insect that did frequently appear was a member of the hawk moth family (Sphingoidea), with grey-brown forewings and delicate pink hind wings, which would fly in and out of the blackness and hover around the light and our drinks. These moths were clearly the original insect dipsomaniacs, for they would hover over the top of a glass and extend their incredibly long proboscises down to the fluid below. This habit was very annoying, for a moth in a glass of beer, or in the bottle itself, sprinkled the liquid with its tiny wing scales. These made it twinkle but also meant that it was undrinkable. Fortunately, the problem was soon solved with characteristic expedition ingenuity, for we found that if the metal top from the bottle was placed on the table and filled with beer a small group of moths would quickly gather round and drink their fill. They then either slumped insensibly to the ground, or flew off erratically in an alcoholic haze. Being good scientists we also tried them on water, which held little attraction, and experimented with several varieties of beer. The moths showed a marked preference for 'Tusker', or, as Meilo put it, 'beer ya dudu na mwananchi' (beer of insects and people), and we couldn't argue with homespun Kora philosophy like that.

In spite of the drought, the buzzing of insects still filled the air during the day producing a background noise that we soon got used to and ceased to hear. It was only when we stopped and listened that we realized that the riverine forest and the bush were reverberating with the deafening hum of the cicadas, a noise that was loud enough to make our heads vibrate if we were in the right position. These insects belong to the plant bug group that have membranous wings (Homoptera), like the frog-hoppers and aphids, in contrast to the shield bug and vicious, biting assassin bugs whose wings are half hard and half membranous (Heteroptera). The cicadas' loud shrill call is only made by the males and is produced when the insect vibrates two, tightly stretched membranes that lie just in front of the abdomen on the underside of the body. The sound reverberates beneath two semi-circular lids that cover the membranes and the changes of pitch which identify individual species are governed by the manner in which these lids are raised and lowered. The sounds are believed to be assembly calls and may also act as a stimulus to the mating instinct, for when a cicada is located it is often the case that a single singing male is accompanied by several silent females. These insects feed from trees by pushing their proboscises into the trunk and drinking the sugary fluids from the sap vessels, pumping up the vital liquids with a large muscular pump that can easily be seen at the base of the mouth parts.

When we tried to find these insects we discovered that their song had a ventriloquial quality that made them difficult to locate, and they also had the annoying habit of moving around the tree just when we thought we had caught them. In fact we obtained far more specimens from the insects attracted to our light at night than we ever found during the day, although when we enlisted the aid of the APU we found that their sharp sense of sound enabled them to trace insects much more effectively than we could. The cry is very distinctive, but the most unusual feature of the cicadas is their breeding cycle. The females lay their eggs in the bark of a tree from which hatch weird larvae with greatly enlarged front legs that they use to burrow into the ground. Depending on species, these larvae then spend up to seventeen years in the subterranean material used for further food for the colony. Like the ants, termites produce winged forms which emerge with the rains and almost darken the sky as they rise in great clouds, pale brown wings fluttering weakly as they disperse.

This rich source of food attracts other insects, amphibians, reptiles, birds and mammals, and indeed the vast numbers of termites that occur throughout these savanna environments provide such a super-abundant source of food that two mammals have evolved on the African continent that are entirely reliant on them. The first of these is the antbear or aardvark (*Orycteropus afer*), which spends the night searching for termite mounds and enters them by tearing holes with its massive claws, in so doing not only obtaining food for itself but also providing homes for a wide variety of other creatures in the empty cavities. That such tiny insects can provide sufficient food to sustain a mammal that weighs up to 80 kg (176 lb) indicates just how abundant the termites are, even if the aardvark needs to travel several kilometres every night to collect them. The second animal which lives off termites is the aardwolf (*Proteles cristatus*), a small (7 to 10 kg, 15 to 22 lb) carnivore with a long handsome mane that resembles the striped hyaena, but which has virtually lost all its molar teeth and feeds exclusively on two genera of termites. These termites live on grasses and forage in the open, so the aardwolf simply has to lick them up and does not need to expend energy on opening hard earth-cased mounds.

Except for the grass-feeding termites, all the other species feed on decomposing vegetation, and particularly on the remains of dead woody vegetation, from twigs and branches to massive trunks. These the termites locate and remove the wood with surprising speed beneath their specially constructed soil casing. These insects thus perform one of the most important ecological functions on the savanna, for it is only when dead material is broken down that the very limited nutrients tied up in vegetation, animal dung and corpses are recycled and made available for further plant growth. The detritivores, as they are called, include termites and dung or carrion beetles. Once they have broken up dead material this is then further decomposed by the bacteria and fungi (the decomposers), thus releasing essential nutrients. Such a cycle is a vital part of any ecological system, and disturbance in the way in which it works may cause total collapse, or at least severe disruption, indicating that although it is the large creatures that the tourist notices, it is the tiny workers which play a far more significant role in achieving a state of balance in these sensitive ecosystems.

Great heat, lack of water and an abundance of predators has resulted in the majority of invertebrates spending most of their lives hidden in burrows, or under bark or litter. There is hardly a single usable space that has not been occupied by some creature, for if they are not capable of burrowing for themselves they live in holes made by something else. This urge to occupy small spaces is one which has always raised difficulties and created dangers for the traveller in the tropical wilderness, and the picture of the hunter shaking his boots out in the morning before he puts them on is an illustration of a sensible precaution, not a figment of the imagination of the writers of adventure stories.

In Kampi ya Ndovu it became a regular ritual to shake out our shorts and boots before we put them on in the morning, and luckily this precaution avoided more than one nasty accident. A much more common danger, though, arose from the tendency of invertebrates with flattened bodies to press themselves between flat surfaces, whether these were rock flakes, pieces of tree bark, plant-drying papers, bedsheets or sleeping bags, a tendency that had been well illustrated by the big pandine scorpion that decided to use Chum's bedding as a quiet hidey-hole. Turning back my own sleeping bag one evening in August I was aware of something wriggling across the white surface and over my hand, which I quickly withdrew with a shudder as I instantly recognized the bright blue and green multiple legs of the 20-cm (8-in) *Scolopendra* centipede. These myriapods are nasty brutes, for their first pair of limbs is folded under the body as two sharply-curved fangs and these are provided with paired poison glands with which they can administer an extremely painful and possibly fatal bite to the unwary. Although the chances of being bitten by many of these creatures are in fact quite remote, I always treat them with great respect, as much from the fear of coming across them in the dark as from the actual dangers they pose.

The work of our entomologists was not just limited to the insects, for a whole variety of other invertebrates fell into the pitfall traps and demanded examination and identification. Paramount amongst these creatures were the spiders, which belonged to at least seventy-one species. As we expected, most of these were forms that lead an earth-bound existence rather than the huge assemblage that is more likely to be recovered on vegetation above ground. The pitfall species were dominated by the jumping spiders (Salticidae), which comprised 22.5 per cent of the total. These often brightly coloured insects are quite small day-hunting species which are equipped with large eyes, like big headlamps, on the front of their heads. These enable them to judge the distance to their prey, which they then leap on and immobilize with their fangs or chelicerae. Probably to the relief of many of the members of the expedition, the large hairy Mygalomorph spiders were only represented by two species, but we may be quite sure that the rock outcrops and similar habitats still hide some of the large amazingly docile species which frequently have a leg span of up to nearly 20 cm (8 in).

Amongst the large group of arachnids to which the spiders belong was a surprising diversity of pseudo-scorpions. These small creatures have flattened abdomens and long clawed limbs on the front of their bodies which they carry in front of them like scorpions, but they lack the tail and sting of the true scorpion. They are predators on small invertebrates, and also often live in association with burrowing mole-rats when they eat the mites that infest the fur of these mammals. These pseudo-scorpions were surprisingly abundant in the bush habitats and of the eight species we found several may prove to be new, for they have been little studied. One of their most remarkable features is their reproductive behaviour, for the female retains the eggs and young in a specially secreted, membranous brood pouch under her body, where they are nourished by a nutritious 'milk' provided by the female from her genital opening. In time the young moult, to emerge into the world as miniature replicas of their parents. It was clear that even these small predators were pretty good at avoiding being eaten, as we discovered that at least one other insect imitated them. When we were sitting around our dining-room table one day I was surprised to see one of these shy creatures walking by, until on closer examination it turned out to be a plant bug that had developed lumps on the end of its long antennae that were exact replicas of the claws of a pseudo-scorpion. These it held out before it in scorpion fashion and even walked the same way.

Because of the dry conditions when we were in Kora, we have only so far found three species of solifuge, wind or camel spiders. These are also arachnids, like the spiders, scorpions and pseudo-scorpions, but have an elongated, segmented abdomen, and a large combined head and thorax, from the front of which arise two massive jaws. They are not poisonous, but obtain their prey by grasping it in their powerful jaws and then tearing it to pieces, grinding the contents into a nutritious fluid which is swallowed by their tiny mouths at the base of the jaws. The commonest species are large robust creatures up to 6 cm (2½ in) long which dig burrows with their jaws, but these solifuges take many forms, from long-legged hairy species which run over the hot sand like bits of thistle-down blown by the wind, to tiny narrow animals that live inside termite mounds. In contrast to the brood care exhibited by the pseudo-scorpions, the solifuges merely lay their eggs in a burrow, which they seal before leaving the eggs to their own developmental devices.

It would be impossible to attempt to collect and describe all the thousands upon thousands of small invertebrates that live in Kora and this was never our intention, for complete catalogues are taxonomic curiosities rather than information of lasting ecological value. What was important, though, was to look at the commonest species, and their distribution and abundance in the major habitats. Collecting in such dry weather was difficult, but we did quickly realize that there were large numbers of snail shells secreted in the litter below the bush vegetation which Chum collected and took back to Nairobi for Martin Pickford to look at. Although Martin's major function in life is to examine and assess the importance of archaeological sites for the National Museum, he is a great authority on the African molluscs. The preliminary shell collections were so promising that he visited Kora as soon as he could get away from his other duties and began his own collecting in November 1983. It has frequently been considered that terrestrial molluscs are poorly represented in dry areas, so it was with great excitement that Martin discovered that Kora was in fact astonishingly rich in these creatures. The molluscs were, however, dominated by a large number of very small species, which probably accounts for the fact that they were poorly known. Significantly the only ones we commonly observed were the stark white shells of long-dead African land snails (*Achatina fulica*), up to 15 cm (6 in) long. The smallest species was a *Thapsiella* which was only 2 mm (0.08 in) in diameter and has yet to be given a scientific name.

One of the most rewarding features of Martin's work was his study of the biogeography, which always yields interesting information on habitats. Basically the molluscs fell into two groups, those that were very widespread in a variety of habitats, and the numerous genera that were limited to desert environments, several of which are found from Africa to Eurasia. Most of the molluscs seemed to be those which occur at lower altitudes, but there was one form that appeared to have migrated down from the highlands. Considering the small area we were surveying in Kora, it was interesting to observe that twenty-one of the hundred mollusc genera recorded in Kenya were represented. Especially exciting, though, was Martin's conclusion that the mollusc fauna seems to indicate that the current dry climate may well be much more recent than we had previously believed. Some valuable collections were also made from dead flood vegetation along the bank of the Tana and its tributary streams. These showed that the snails which carry the blood parasite, bilharzia, were very common in these situations, a warning to our biologists who were investigating the stiller aquatic habitats.

There were few signs of molluscs actually in the Tana's brown waters, no doubt because the large quantities of suspended silt make it impossible for most gastropods (snails with coiled shells) and bivalves (molluscs with two shells) to keep their respiratory apparatuses clean. The only representatives of these groups that we found were *Aspatharia hartmanni*, a common and widespread form in Kenya which was found at Marenge, and the much rarer gastropod *Melanoides tuberculata*, collected from temporary aquatic habitats near Baboon Hill, and in the Monune lugga.

In order to study most of the invertebrates we had to look for them, but there were also some easily observed situations that illustrated the way in which extreme environments like Kora lead to the evolution of forms restricted to specific sites and life styles. One such habitat was the striking, shiny purple trunks of the large *Sterculia rhynchocarpa*, which were scattered irregularly through the bush and at the base of the outcrops. Almost from the first day we sighted them we were struck by the fact that much of the bright outer bark had been stripped away, and that the surface was covered with masses of brown tubes. These structures were hemispherical in section, and consisted of a tube of silk to which had been attached a dense layer of brown faecal pellets. In many cases over 30 per cent of the surface of the trunk was covered with these tubes, and in excess of 80 per cent of the outer bark had been eaten away. When we stripped the tubes we found the remains of moth pupae at their ends, but since none of them were alive we were unable to discover what moth had been responsible for ravaging the trees. On the same trees we also found some large, pale fawn plant bugs, belonging to the same group as the 'cotton stainers' (pests of cotton), while further exploration revealed their brilliant scarlet young in the litter at the base of the trees and in the star-shaped fruits. In both cases these insects were found nowhere else, and appeared to be restricted to this one species of tree. No doubt defences on the part of the tree allowed these insects to feed on this valuable food resource without competition from other species.

many years of lonely wandering in the African bush. For us his presence was a tonic, for he epitomized the people that have dedicated their lives to work in the bush, despite the fact that their knowledge is so often unappreciated and their contribution to natural history unrecognized.

Terence is no longer as young as he was, so we tried to stop him doing too much, but this is never easy with old timers that have done and seen it all. After one trip to the west of the Reserve, he did not look too well and on our return was sick and seemed very frail, so Nicola put him to bed and nursed him until she felt he was well enough to go back to George's camp. Then in August he gave us a real fright when a party went out on to the Monune lugga track with the intention of walking inland and then returning in a wide arc to the vehicles. I had remained in camp and was writing notes at the table when I heard a Land Rover coming down the track at great speed, blasting its horn, our prearranged signal for an emergency or incoming injured. We rushed to the gate to meet a pale-faced Peter, who yelled out of the window, 'Terence has collapsed out in the bush, because some damned fool took him off away from the main party.' We rushed to load the stretcher and the ever-ready emergency medical bag, while Meilo and John quickly prepared flasks of tea and a pack of biscuits. I remained behind in case anything else came up, and Nicola left with Peter and other help to try and get the Land Rover off the track into the bush to pick him up, for the sun was already low in the sky. I waited, wondering how bad he was and thinking at the same time that, if he were going to die, this was surely where he would choose to go when the time came. After what seemed like hours the vehicles returned with the walking party, including Terence who, though very pale, could manage a smile and an apology for 'causing all this trouble'. We laughed with relief, thankful that he was only a bit dehydrated and tired. It was also a relief to know that our emergency drill had been put to the test and worked like clockwork. All our team had performed splendidly, even though some needed calming down over what had clearly been an avoidable situation.

When I had met George on my reconnaissance in 1982, we had agreed that we should site our camp out of range of his lions. In eighteen months, though, lions tend to move, so that by the time we settled in to Kampi ya Ndovu they had preceded us. While Tim Palmer put the finishing touches to the camp they patrolled up and down outside the half-completed fence, rending the night air with their throaty roars, a game they continued to play after we arrived. They seldom showed themselves, though, and we were usually only aware of their presence in the early morning or late afternoon. Then a loud 'ee-agh, ee-agh, ee-agh' would issue from the bush close to the gate and we would close it hastily in case they were anticipating dropping in for a snack. Lions, like humans, do not like walking through the nasty thorn bush when there is a nice elephant or camel track at hand, or even more conveniently a road. Thus even when we didn't hear them, we would examine the road with the APU every morning to look for spoor, and there we would invariably see their characteristic trail – great, broad, rounded paw prints placed close together and almost in a straight line. There would perhaps also be several sets of smaller prints left by the young ones, which meandered back and forth as they had played with each other during the course of their nocturnal perambulations.

We were really very fortunate, for the lions appeared to be as anxious to avoid us as we were to avoid them. The two most frequent residents were Grow and Glow, who had decided that the mouth of the Monune lugga was an ideal spot to set up a home base. Plenty of game animals came down to drink here, providing a potential source of food, and during the height of the drought there was also the possibility of domestic animals. When the Somalis brought their herds to drink during the day, any animal that was too weak to walk would be left behind – these pathetically thin creatures would lie under a bush, unable to feed or even to get to the water to drink. Sometimes they would lie there for two or three days before the lions eventually killed them, or if they were close to the river's edge we would find impressions of crocodiles' bellies in the sand, indicating that they had dragged the unfortunate animals back to the water, where they drowned them. The crocodiles' patience is an important feature of their feeding behaviour, for in spite of their seemingly powerful jaws, they are unable to eat fresh meat from large carcases covered with very elastic skin. In order to feed they have to wait for their prey to decompose. They will then grab a mouthful and, by rapidly twisting the body from side to side in a spiral action, tear off lumps of putrid flesh which they then bolt down with a flick of their massive, scaly heads. Watching abandoned animals was dreadful for us, for our armed APU men were required to account for every round of their ammunition, and it was not considered appropriate to use these expensive materials to put domestic animals out of their misery.

Grow and Glow were not only handsome beasts, but also appeared to have an intelligent sense of humour. Sky Alibhai and Gill Campbell, Ken Campbell's wife, had started their small-mammal trapping programme quite close to our camp and had gradually extended their zone of operations to the Monune lugga. They went to the lugga one evening and set a 200-m (650-ft) line of traps along the edge of the dry river-bed at a point where it swept in a large arc westwards, having first checked with Osman and Dominic of the APU that there were no signs of lions. The next morning they returned at first light in a Land Rover and, as they rounded the corner, there, lying by the first traps, were Grow and Glow, peacefully resting on the red earth. With some gentle persuasion they moved the lions a little further down the lugga, far enough for Sky to be able to emerge from the vehicle and check the traps, closely accompanied by Osman at the front and Dominic at the back, rifles at the ready. As Sky moved forward and Gill followed driving the Land Rover, the lions watched with great curiosity, but they eventually rose and sauntered off down the lugga, their bellies swinging gently from side to side as they went. Sky breathed a sigh of relief and proceeded down the line of traps at a faster pace. Close to the end of the trap line the river-bed took a sharp turn to the right, and as he followed it to look at the last of the traps, there, lying next to the last trap, were the two lionesses, heads raised, their large golden eyes watching the vehicle and the three pedestrians with great interest.

Whether their presence was an accident we will never know, but it seems more than probable that the lions had followed the scent of humans, and the smell of the traps and the bait they contained. Sky completed his trap round quickly, as the vehicle and a few loud shouts persuaded the two lionesses to move off into the shelter of the fringing *Salvadora* bush, where they flopped down for a spot of sleep, an activity that seems to take up a large proportion of a lion's life.

Detailed studies of the larger animals were not a part of our programme, partly because one can do little in a short time, but more particularly because there was no place for individual investigations within our overall task. The information we did gather on the larger species was obtained as a result of members recording sitings as they went about their other work. People would note the position of animals in relation to their route and the distance from base camp, giving a location for Chum to plot on our base maps. Exact positions were unnecessary, provided sitings could be recorded by reference to the kilometre-square grid that had been superimposed on our base map by the RGS cartographer.

The presence of George's lions tended to obscure the fact that the dense bush of Kora is the home of a large number of other predators. Amongst these was the elegant cheetah (*Acinonyx jubatus*), which we saw frequently, especially in the western and central parts of the Reserve, a pattern of distribution that reflected those areas frequented by pastoralists rather than the occurrence of a particularly suitable habitat. This long, slim-bodied cat with its fine spots has elegant black tear stripes running down its face from the inner corner of the eye to the lower jaw. It was formerly distributed in a belt from western India, through Arabia, along the coast of north and west Africa, and then through the savanna belt to the southern tip of Africa. Today it has disappeared from its eastern range and even within the African continent its numbers have been greatly reduced in all areas, mirroring the continuing disappearance of the small antelopes on which it feeds. Its wide distribution in Kora would surprise many people, for this fleet-footed creature is generally associated with more open grasslands where it can run down its prey with an explosive burst of speed. The cheetah is capable of up to 112 km (70 miles) an hour over short distances, although studies have now indicated that only 37 per cent of chases are successful when hunting adults, a figure that rises to 76 per cent when they are preying on juveniles. In Kora there were none of the grazers of the open plains, except for an occasional Grant's gazelle (*Gazella granti petersi*), but the abundant Kirk's dik-dik (*Madoqua kirkii*), although only about 40 cm (16 in) high at the shoulder, provided a suitable alternative for the cheetah and would be supplemented by the young of larger antelopes, guinea fowl, francolin and even hares. Large mammals like the cheetah are largely limited by the availability of suitably sized prey rather than by habitats, and the speed with which they disappeared into the low bush whenever we sighted them demonstrated just how well adapted they were to the Kora vegetation.

181

munities dominated by grazers, to those largely consisting of browers. This suggested cycle is in fact at least in part confirmed by the increasing level of damage to the bushland of Kora during the present drought. This has been partly caused by natural tree death, which in some areas has approached 50 per cent, and partly by the concentration of elephants in the park, which George considers have reached a record level of 700 individuals.

The herbivorous large mammals of Kora are dominated by browsers which, although not abundant, are spread fairly evenly through the *Acacia-Commiphora* bushland. The most abundant of the browsers is the tiny Kirk's dik-dik, one of three species limited to arid regions of Africa and with a distribution similar to the oryx in the Horn of Africa and southwest Africa. In northern Kenya, Guenther's dik-dik occurs in some of the same areas as Kirk's, but this was not so in the Kora region where only Kirk's is present. These small, 40 cm-high (16 in) herbivores have a tuft of hair on their foreheads and only the males bear short horns. Their most unusual feature, which distinguishes them from all the other antelopes, is their snout-like proboscis which has two slits at its end thought to act as a cooling device in these hot regions. The dik-diks live in small family groups consisting of a male and female and their young. Each group maintains a strict territory that is demarcated by tiny black scent marks deposited on the ends of twigs or grass stems by the males. The animals have special scent-making glands for this purpose, known as preorbital glands, which are sited just in front of the eye. They also use their dung as a territorial marker, depositing it in small piles which they then scrape with their sharp hooves so that a large depression over a metre (3 ft) across is created. This activity ensures that the family group know the bounds of the area that they live in very well, and also that other intruding dik-dik are in no doubt that the area is occupied.

We came across these charming little mammals everywhere we went and they would watch us with interest as we wandered through the bush and became almost as tame as the caracal. However, if we took liberties and approached too close, the male would utter a loud, high-pitched whistle which would be repeated several times as the group bounded away through the bush. Their dung sites were very obvious patches of bare ground throughout the bush, and appeared to be equally distinctive to other mammals, for we often found their dung deposited in the dik-dik's diminutive lavatories.

Much less common, but very obvious, were the much larger lesser kudu (*Tragelaphus imberbis*), and the gerenuk or Waller's gazelle (*Litocranius walleri*), both of which are specialized browsing herbivores that are limited to the Somalian region (encompassing eastern Ethiopia, Somalia and northern Kenya), and an area extending through Kenya to northern Tanzania. The males and females of the lesser kudu are markedly different, the males being very dark with white lateral stripes and further white chevrons on the throat, while the female, although also bearing white stripes, is basically a rich red-brown colour. Only the males have the slightly radiating twisted horns that are nearly a metre (3 ft) long. Their diet consists of a wide variety of plants, including grass, but tree shoots and fruits seem to predominate. It is possible that kudu often feed at night when the water content of their food is high.

The browser par excellence of these bushlands is undoubtedly the gerenuk, for its long narrow muzzle enables it to 'whiffle' along branches, selecting the tiny shoots and deftly avoiding the spines and hooks. Its greatest feature, though, is its shape, for it is one of the oddest-looking antelopes of all. Its body is a pleasant warm russet-brown and has fairly normal proportions, but the neck is incredibly long and narrow and is surmounted by a small slender head, crowned in the male by a pair of elegant lyre-shaped horns. This long neck serves an important function, for it allows the gerenuk to outreach all the other antelopes in search of some succulent morsel. By standing on its hind legs, its total reach is extended to over 2 m (6 ft) and in this position its narrow muzzle can reach through the thickest thorn barrier to pluck a wide variety of shoots, a selective diet that, together with a specialized physiology, makes the gerenuk completely independent of water. These antelopes are territorial animals which mark their areas with preorbital gland secretions like the dik-dik, but they do not employ dung piles.

Oddly enough, the gerenuk's extraordinary adaptations for feeding in these dense thorny habitats have been repeated in another species in the Horn of Africa. In a small area of Somalia there is an antelope known as the dibatag (*Ammodorcas clarkei*), which belongs to a different tribe from the gerenuk and yet has evolved the same characteristics – long legs and an elongated slender neck. Indeed, if one is looking for a good example of the powerful role that the pressures of environmental selection play in the evolution of mammals, it would be difficult to find a better one than the convergent adaptations of these two species of arid-bush-dwelling antelopes. The fact that they are not paralleled by another similar creature in southwest Africa is probably due to the absence of the dense thorn scrub that is such a dominant feature of the landscape in the northeast.

The very tops of the trees were out of reach of all but the giraffe and the elephant, both of whom have a remarkable reach, the former with its long neck and sinuous tongue, and the latter with its long trunk that can extend high above its back and pluck succulent morsels with astonishing dexterity. If an elephant cannot reach food with its trunk, it also has the ability to knock over large trees, either by pushing them over with its massive forehead, or by using its coiled trunk like a hardy battering ram. This type of elephant damage is well known in other parts of Africa, but was relatively uncommon in Kora until the advent of the drought and also perhaps until elephants tended to congregate in Kora to escape pressure from poachers outside. That such pressures do exist is indicated by the fact that we found the elephants to be extremely shy, for in spite of observing their footprints daily along the track from our camp and further inland, we only saw them on the ground on two occasions. We did, however, sight four groups from the air close to George's camp when Fred Pertet and Pat Hamilton brought a small WCMD aircraft to Kora. The giraffe were much more common, though scattered. Their browse lines on the trees were noticeable in many areas, for when a tree succeeds in growing beyond their reach the crown radiates outwards, while the lower part takes on an hour-glass shape. In some cases the underside of the canopy is quite flat, marking the point where the mouths of the taller bulls can just keep the tree trimmed like a topiary hedge. When you come across these massive tall creatures in the bush they are usually standing quite immobile except for a long, handsome, swishing, black-tipped tail and an occasional flick of their ears. Even now when they are so familiar, I still find something slightly comic about them. These animals raised an interesting problem of identification for us. Although they were evidently the southern Masai giraffe which has a jigsaw-like pattern, quite a few of them appeared to have markings that were intermediate with the straight-edged, more regular checker-board pattern of the northern reticulate giraffe. Since both species of giraffe do occur together in places north of the Tana, it seems unlikely that there are hybrids present in Kora, but I have long since stopped being dogmatic about such matters in the wilds of Africa.

While the grass cover below the spiny trees is quite sparse, it is capable of supporting a few oryx and scattered groups of warthog (*Phacochoerus aethiopicus*), the widespread African savanna pig which will suddenly explode from a thicket or its burrow and dash away with its tail held erect, the hairy tip just showing above the grass. The male warthogs have curved tusks that are often immense and curl up over their cheeks, making them look as if they have permanent grins on their faces as they regard you from the bush for a few seconds before the group bolts for cover. In spite of their threatening appearance and the great ugly warts that sprout from their faces as a protection for the eyes, these pigs can be tamed very easily and, although they often forget that their tusks are very sharp, they will remain playful and friendly to adulthood, even after they have returned to the wild. A call of 'Hello piggies' in Tsavo would bring a group of ex-orphans hurtling out of the bush to indulge in their favourite game of 'push the visitor over'.

The riverine bush provided a haven for many mammals, even above the Kora Falls where it was only a narrow strip. Most of the animals here were visitors who had come to water or to feed on the leaves or fruits which remained available long after they had disappeared from the bush beyond. An exception was the common water-buck (*Kobus ellipsiprymnus*), which is entirely restricted to the vicinity of water where grass, its main source of food, is available for most of the year. This chunky beast reaches up to 1.3 m (4 ft) in height at the shoulder and a big male may weigh as much as 250 kg (550 lb). Its fur is long and pale grey, with russet tones on the flank and neck and a white elliptic ring on the rump, which gives it its species name. The male is horned, bearing a pair of robust ringed horns that sweep backwards and upwards, and with large black-tipped expressive ears placed either side of them. Family groups consisting of a male, several females and their stockily-built young, which are pale and very furry, were a common sight along the river road.

The riverine bush was also primate country, for groups of the vervet monkey or Tumbili (*Cercopithecus aethiops*) occupied most of the stands of taller trees, and like all their relatives showed immense curiosity at our appearance on the scene. They soon learned that there were easy pickings from the rubbish pits around our camp and would sit watching us from the trees, waiting their opportunity to pop down for a snack. The larger males, with their bright, pale blue scrotums, handsome pale grey-green fur and white undersides, would peer out from behind a branch and jerk their heads back out of sight if we moved our heads in imitation. We did not welcome their presence, though, for semi-tame primates can be a great nuisance stealing food and generally creating havoc when they come to live around human habitations. Encouraging these comical mammals was most definitely taboo.

The riverine forest was also home to baboons, represented in Kora by two very different forms, the olive baboon (*Papio cynocephalus anubis*) and the yellow baboon (*Papio cynocephalus cynocephalus*), both of which are known in Swahili as nyani. The former has a generally more westerly distribution and the latter more easterly, but in the centre of their distributions there is considerable overlap between the two subspecies, and hybrids have been reported. They are very distinct in build for the olive baboon is a thick-set dark animal, and the yellow baboon a longer-legged more slender creature. It is not yet clear in what way these two subspecies differ but we noticed that, although they both came to water, the yellow baboon lived near the outcrops but not on them, while the olive baboon was a more common resident of the rock islands themselves. Their ability to survive in these dry regions has a great deal to do with their almost completely omnivorous diet, which includes everything from plants, fruits and tubers to insects, scorpions and lizards. They even eat the young of antelopes, which they search out in the first few days of their lives when they 'lie out' hidden by their mothers in the vegetation.

The larger mammals were such an obvious feature of Kora that it is easy to think of them as dominant. This is, however, not true, for the smaller creatures outnumber them by several orders of magnitude. This may not seem important, but when we think of relative numbers in terms of their day-to-day impact, it becomes clear that all creatures need to be considered if the full picture is to be understood. One way of assessing any particular species is to consider the speed with which it turns over its numbers or total weight. The massive elephant, for example, is very large, but it also lives a long time so this species only turns over, or replaces, about 5 per cent of its biomass each year. In contrast, a small, shorter-lived antelope will turn over up to 60 per cent of its biomass each year. If this analysis is extended to really small mammals, or to birds, reptiles and even insects, we see that these species are capable of turning over their biomass several times in one year, and therefore rival even the elephant in the amount of material that they process in that time.

We were more than familiar with the lizards, and especially the large Agama lizards (*Agama agama*), whose males have brilliant orange heads and metallic blue bodies in contrast to the pale fawn bodies of the much smaller females with their almost white, striped throats. The males are intensely territorial, and patrolled around our camp bobbing their bright heads up and down on any available vantage point, on occasions so intent upon their signalling that we nearly trod on them. One couple quickly became part of our life, and we christened the male 'Maggie' and his quieter mate 'Dennis'. I was in fact instrumental in saving Maggie's life one day. A large white-browed coucal, a relative of the cuckoo, had taken up residence just outside our fence and hunted all manner of quite large prey, although it had a clumsy gait and almost pathetic flight. One morning I was walking across the site when I saw the coucal dash under a bush, followed by the sounds of frantic struggles. On investigation I found that the bird had grabbed Maggie by the head and was attempting, with great difficulty, to gulp the lizard down its throat, while Maggie thrashed its tail and legs vigorously. 'He's got Maggie', I yelled as I flung myself under the bush and grabbed the bird, prizing the frantic lizard from its throat. They both departed hastily, the lizard to secrete itself under a log, and the coucal back to its bush where it clucked angrily.

Amongst the many interesting creatures in Kora, none showed a more distinct separation in their preferred habitats than the two species of terrapin. One (*Pelusios sinuatus*) was restricted to the river, where we would see the black, flattened bodies of these creatures lined up along a log as they emerged from the water to take in the heat of the early-morning sun. Yet inland in the seasonal pools there was a quite different terrapin (*Pelomedusa subrufa*), which revelled in the short season of abundant food and then retreated into the mud and lay there in a cavity in the hard soil until the rains returned.

Feeding on all these smaller creatures were that other group of predators without which no description of the wilderness is complete, for the first question you are always asked on your return to the busy world outside is whether you have seen any snakes. The truth, of course, is that they are for the large part secretive and not often spotted unless you have the eye of a real snake-catcher, when it rapidly becomes apparent that the bush is alive with these fascinating reptiles. During really dry conditions, though, the snakes are few and far between, for when food is short they quickly retreat underground and lie low until conditions aloft improve. Even so, snakes certainly enlivened life in camp. During the first few days several long, slim sand snakes slithered through the wire and made their way across the ground with budding herpetologists in hot pursuit. Once cornered, however, the snake would produce a loud hiss and its pursuer would become less keen, even though these are only back-fanged snakes and just mildly venomous.

Ken Campbell came the closest to getting a nasty surprise when the fish party found a small black snake on the beach and persuaded it to crawl into a plastic bag which they brought back to camp. 'Hey, Malcolm,' they called, 'what's this?' I grasped the bag and peered at the slim black reptile, immediately noticing its narrow head. 'I know it only looks like a harmless house snake', I said, 'but if you look at its head you will see that it has two long fangs lying along the angle of the lower jaw, which makes it a burrowing viper (*Atractaspis microlepidota*).' This nasty little brute has such long fangs that it can bite with its mouth closed and even slash independently to left or right, impaling a finger or any other bit of your anatomy that is alongside. To confirm this point I removed the snake from the bag and held it down while I elevated the long fangs – a drop of venom dripped from the end as I did so. Small though the drop was, this venom will cause local death of tissue and leave a nasty wound, or even result in the loss of a digit. This snake provided a valuable lesson to all concerned and in future people left things well alone if they didn't know what they were. This was, perhaps predictably, the last snake Ken brought in.

In the bush itself we were disappointed at the apparent lack of snakes, which were undoubtedly quietly aestivating in nooks and crannies. Camp, though, surprisingly produced more excitement in December 1983 when Chris West and his entomological buddies were startled by the sound of a guinea fowl yelling its head off just outside. Investigation showed that a large African python (*Python sebae*) was busy strangling the life out of the bird. The snake was frightened off and the dead bird was eagerly given to the cooks for dinner, for the meat supply was then down to two tins of corned beef. But our greatest excitement of all was when Mike Keating came out of our hut and yelled, 'Malcolm, there's a snake under your bed.' I entered the hut quietly but could not see the snake for all the rubbish under the bed, so we agreed that I would stand outside with a stick ready to grab it when it was driven out. No sooner had Mike Keating disturbed the accumulated debris, than a narrow head appeared under the wall, which I pinned down with the stick as it emerged. And that was where I made my mistake, for as I pinned it down I was immediately aware that I had taken on an eastern spitting cobra (*Naja pallida*), its bright claret colour and the black band round its neck making it quite unmistakable. As I watched, the snake slid smoothly under the inadequate hold of my stick, raised its hood, threw its head backwards, and spat at me. Fortunately I had thrown myself backwards, taking the venom on my legs and not in my eyes, for it would have produced instantaneous, even if only temporary, blindness. Meanwhile the snake had disappeared into the base of a large tree just 1 m (3 ft) from the wall, and try as we might we could not dislodge it and in fact never saw it again. But for several nights afterwards I would suddenly wake in the early hours and peer round with my torch, finally looking under my bed to see if it had, by chance, come back again.

Although the tourists come to Kenya to look at the large mammals and birds, there is a multitude of small vertebrates at the bottom of the size scale which are of immense importance, both in terms of their numbers and because of their impact on the local habitats. Amongst the most numerous of these were the rodents which Sky and Gill had come to study, for they are not only an important group of dominantly herbivorous animals, but also support diurnal and nocturnal mammalian and avian predators at higher levels in the food chains. There are considerable problems involved in studying these creatures, for we seldom see them and they have to be trapped. In order to do this successfully, the bait must be attractive and it is necessary to know something about where an animal lives if the traps are to be positioned in the right place. The potential number of species that may be caught in this way is large and we decided it was necessary to use more than one trapping technique, employing both large and small snap traps which would kill the animals, and live traps which would catch them without harming them so that they could be released after capture, and with luck recaptured on a second occasion. Releasing trapped animals is of vital importance for anyone studying rodents, for if they are killed their removal from the site will encourage other members of the same species to move into the vacant spaces, and any estimate of total numbers will be inflated by this immigration. Moreover, if live traps are used, the animals captured can be marked before they are released, providing valuable information on their movements and activity if they are caught again, in addition to providing reasonable estimates of the density of the species. One disadvantage of trapping is that it is labour-intensive work, for it takes a long time to bait and set a large number of traps and in the environment we were in they had to be tied down so they were not dragged away by roving scavengers and predators. Moreover, in these hot dry habitats virtually all the rodents, except the squirrels, are nocturnal, so the main trapping effort was in the evening when anyone not engaged in other studies was pressed into service setting traps, including Nicola, Hamish and Mike Keating, who were thus given an opportunity to join in the scientific work.

During the course of his studies Sky sampled the small-mammal populations in the riverine bush, on the rock outcrops, and in the *Acacia-Commiphora* woodland, including both densely vegetated sites and those on more open grassland. The total number of species trapped was twelve, including three species of gerbil, five species of mice, one dormouse, two species of shrew and the tiny bush squirrel (*Paraxerus ochraceus ganana*), which was especially common in the riverine bush adjacent to Kampi ya Ndovu. In these dry environments trapping is a frustrating business, for compared with temperate environments where rodent densities in undisturbed grassland may reach 250 per hectare (2½ acres), in Kora we obtained figures of less than 5 animals per hectare. This low density is reflected in the trapping-success figures, which are traditionally expressed as the percentage success for the traps set. In order to ensure that the animals were not shy of the traps that had been placed in the bush, they were all pre-baited with food for one night before they were set to catch. A total of 3300 trap nights yielded 300 animals, an overall success of just over 9 per cent. However, this figure does not provide a fair representation of the total picture, for there was considerable variation between the habitats, with a figure of 3 per cent in the riverine *Salvadora* bush, 5 per cent in the *Acacia-Commiphora* bush and a much more encouraging 15 per cent on the rock outcrops. Though these figures rose slightly when calculated on the basis of animals caught on the first night (respectively 5, 6 and 22 per cent), what these observations confirmed was that the outcrops and the pediments around their bases were the most productive habitats, a finding reflected in their comat the ever-helpful police station and come on to Kora in their Suzuki, using the map that I had provided to indicate the location of the Kora drums. We arrived back in about three hours and settled our visitors in with beer cooled in the river, a method which was not a patch on the flasks of ice they had carried with them in typical well-organized United Nations' fashion. By 8.30 pm George and Giovanni had still not arrived, so Nigel and Hamish set out to look for them, finally locating them at the Kora-Mwingi junction. They had decided to spend the night here after trying the Monune track and then rejecting it as the wrong road when they were only 50 m (160 ft) from the river junction. They all returned at about 10.30 pm, tired and dusty, but we were relieved that the system had worked yet again, and that we now had our NASA man Brent Holben in camp, who would be joined in a few days by his partner Chris Justice. The new arrivals tucked into a nourishing Meilo stew before we all turned in and the sounds of conversation died to be replaced by the mysterious noises of the African night.

The NASA team were primarily interested in collecting information on the ground, so called 'ground truth', which would enable them to interpret the satellite images which they had been working on in Washington. They were particularly interested in vegetation types, and the general physiography, which they wanted to look at in detail. Ground studies of this kind are proving of increasing importance, for although the images from space are very clear, and can provide gross detail, the fine particulars can only be filled in when the ground information has been confirmed. In addition to the aerial photographs that we already had in base camp, Brent had brought with him images of Kora derived from both Landsat and meteorological satellites. These two imaging systems differ both in the degree of ground detail they can provide and in the time interval between successive images of a particular area.

Since 1972 there have been four Landsat satellites which orbit 920 km (575 miles) above the Earth on north-south tracks inclined at 9° to the poles, viewing a strip 185 km (115 miles) wide. These satellites circle the Earth every 103 minutes 26 seconds, completing 14 orbits a day, each of which provides a 14 per cent overlap between adjacent tracks. Landsat images are not like ordinary photographs, for the 'pictures' the satellites provide are based on a multispectral scanner (MSS) which measures solar energy being reflected from the Earth in four wavebands. The principle on which this instrument works is that different surfaces, such as vegetation, bare rock and water, reflect solar energy differently in each of the wavebands, so recording these differences will give an image of the ground. In this way it is possible to learn a great deal about a remote area of the Earth from examining satellite images.

The information from the MSS is digitised on board the satellite as 256 possible intensity levels for each waveband, providing very fine detail. After digitization the information is then transmitted to ground stations, where it is recorded and subsequently processed for use by groups such as ourselves who are interested in these lofty images of their study areas. The finest detail provided by the MSS system is an area of 0.45 hectares (0.125 acres), known as a pixcel, which measures 57 × 79 m (187 × 259 ft), and these units make up an individual picture or scene which covers an area of 185 km² (71 sq miles). One of these scenes is taken by the satellite every 27.6 seconds, and is made up of 2250 lines, each of which is composed of 3240 pixels, a total of an incredible 7.29 million pixels on every scene.

A satellite image from Landsat is a 'false colour' image, made up by super-imposing films of the different spectral bands selected. This digitized information is available on computer tapes, which may be manipulated to enhance their clarity or to emphasize different features. Also, since the information is recorded as individual units or pixels, it is possible to blow up one or more of these to look for local detail. Brent and Chris used a Landsat 3 image of Kora taken on 14 June 1979 to produce a sub-image of a quarter of a single scene that covered the Kora National Reserve. On this enhanced colour image the red tones were associated with the green vegetation along the Tana River and lugga fringes, the blue tones represented the dormant vegetation, with a strong contribution from underlying surface material below the sparse tree canopies, while the light areas represented the regions of bare soil and rock. Looking at this image in detail we could see the fairly abundant red areas of green vegetation, resulting from the brief and hardly adequate short rains, and the pale area of the alluvial material in the northwest of Kora where our transects 4a and 4b were sited. The large areas of bare rock oriented north-south, which represented the Pre-Cambrian Basement complex, also showed up well, with all the major outcrops clearly outlined. But the most remarkable feature of the image was the three black areas that represented land that had been subject to uncontrolled burning by pastoralists in an attempt to stimulate new grass growth. All three of these areas were limited to their west by the line of a lugga which had acted as a fire break, the two areas outside the Reserve being limited by the Mwitamisyi lugga, while the central area located in the Reserve itself had been prevented from spreading by another lugga. The image showed a plume of smoke still rising from this burnt patch and drifting to the north.

The detail provided by Landsat images is very good, but since they are not available regularly over a long period, they did not provide the seasonal picture that interested Brent, Chris, and above all ourselves. This is where the meteorological satellites come into their own for they can provide information at much more frequent intervals. The American NOAA meteorological satellites have a nearly circular orbit between 810 and 826 km (506 and 516 miles) above the Earth's surface, inclined at 99° to the Equator (i.e. 9° to the poles). Their advantage is that their orbits are said to be sun-synchronous, i.e. they pass over the same point of the Earth each day and thus provide a regular series of daily pictures which enable weather and surface conditions to be monitored repeatedly. The European Meteosat satellite has additional advantages since it lies in a so-called geostationary orbit, which has been devised so as to relate to the Earth's rotation in such a way that the satellite appears to remain stationary over Europe and Africa. On the other hand, the American NOAA satellites provide images with a better ground resolution than the European Meteosat system, although the detail is not as good as in a Landsat image.

We could hardly believe our eyes when Brent laid out pictures taken by the NOAA meteorological satellite on the dining room table at base camp, for they showed images that reflected the march of the seasons. We were particularly fortunate for we had to hand images from the American 7 NOAA-TIROS Satellite, which has provided meteorological data since 1972. It gave us continuous cover of the Reserve, obtained by integrating pictures taken every three days over a period of a month and electronically eliminating cloud cover. These new and exciting images showed us the brief rainy season prior to May 1983, when plant growth was rapid, and the onset of drier conditions, with the green vegetation retreating up the slope to the highlands in the west. Eventually the red tones representing green vegetation in the riverine fringe virtually disappeared as the drought advanced, and they would not reappear until the rains broke again.

Our first day with Brent was spent looking at aerial and satellite pictures, and identifying places of interest which he wanted to check out on the ground. Although there was little greenery, gross features such as the rock outcrops showed up clearly on the pictures. Our first port of call was Kiume, where Brent could get a good idea of the general features of the landscape and the vegetation differences on the rock-strewn pediments which surrounded the outcrops. Robin Payne had remained behind after Andrew and Peter had returned to Nairobi to spend a few days in the Herbarium, so he accompanied us on our introductory visits to the major habitats. After he had been in Kora a couple of days, Brent declared to our delight that he had initially thought that I had probably exaggerated the interest and importance of the Reserve, but that he was now convinced that the information that we had collected would enable them to interpret the space images with much greater accuracy than had previously been possible. Indeed, after he and Chris Justice returned to Nairobi, Harvey Croze of UNEP/GEMS had flown them over the whole Tana river basin, which prompted Brent's comforting observation, 'Do you realize that Kora is virtually the only undisturbed area of *Acacia-Commiphora* bush in the whole Tana river basin?'

In addition to his concern with habitats, Brent was also interested in the pastoralists, for whether we like it or not, they are an integral and increasingly important part of the Kora scene. On 5 September we took him to Osako village beyond the eastern boundary, where he could see a Korakora village and observe families of Somalis who had brought their animals down to luggas to drink. Just beyond the Reserve boundary we were all involved in one of the common dramas of the bush, for we were flagged down by a young Somali, who told us that his father was very ill. He took us to their camp and into a low hut, where we found an old man, who explained that he hadn't urinated for two days. His lower abdomen was tense and distended so I decided that we should take him on to the dispensary in Osako. Unfortunately when we arrived we could only find an assistant, who said he could not treat the old man and that he should wait until the next day when the doctor visited from Balambala on the other side of the river. I explained this to the sick man, but in spite of our remonstrations he insisted on going back to his camp on the grounds that if he was going to be sick he might as well be sick at home. So we returned him to his hut and wondered for days afterwards if he had ever gone back to the dispensary. In spite of the great strides made in health care since Kenya's independence in 1963, being sick in the bush is still a serious business.

During our examination of the satellite pictures Brent had been somewhat perplexed by small patches of green vegetation where everything else appeared to be dry and parched. As we drove along the river to a regular Somali watering place, we located one of these spots on the map – when I saw where it was I realized that there was a good reason for it to look green. My suspicions proved correct when we rounded a bend and saw the long mass of jumbled boulders that makes up the steep-sided ridge of Katania, for all over the upper slopes and crest of the ridge there was a virtual forest of the great tree spurge (Euphorbia nyikae), the lobed and spiny branches arching upwards like green bony fingers. The detail on a Landsat image is not good enough to discriminate individual trees, but a large stand of one species will be clearly observable. Although the animal population is not discernible, once the dominant ground features have been identified on a satellite image, field knowledge can tell you what other plants and animals may be associated with them. In the case of these jumbled boulders, the large, shaggy rock hyraxes that were watching us from their urine-streaked boulders would be preyed on by leopards and large black eagles (Aquila verreauxii), while there would be many species of mongoose preying on the characteristic spiny mice. As the satellite image also indicates the amount of bare ground, this gives a measure of the degree to which the area has been disturbed which can be used to predict the effect on the flora and fauna without visiting the site, provided this type of country has already been inventoried and described in broad detail.

We found a group of Somalis at the river, just before the rocky ridge of Katania crossed the track, and drove down to the bank to talk to them. They did not look pleased to see us, for it was clear that we had a group of the APU with us and they must have been aware that a unit from Ted Gosse's Ngong team were operating in the Reserve and arresting the elders for illegal grazing. There were now so many Somalis in the Reserve that their presence could no longer be ignored. We approached the group carefully, for we had been told that three armed Shifta had entered the area about three weeks before. They had apparently buried their arms and were moving about with the herdsmen looking, we suspected, for elephant and rhino tracks. The Somalis produced their identity cards (kipande), which indicated that they had come from Garissa and Muddo Gashi in the north, driven no doubt by the lack of grazing. They had no right to have their animals in the Reserve, so they were told that they must move to the other side of the river, which they assured us with a grin that they were just about to cross when we stumbled upon them. Osman,

such time as the population as a whole is willing to recognize this fact and institute controls, the world is doomed to famines of ever-increasing ferocity, until the day will come when human numbers, combined with the natural and unavoidable effects of climate on food availability, will produce a disaster that will make the dangers of atomic war look like a mild dose of flu.

Of course such problems do not just face the developing nations, for even though populations have begun to stabilize themselves in the countries of the developed world, most of their governments have not yet 'grasped the nettle' and instituted programmes directed at maintaining an optimum population size. Under these circumstances it is not surprising that the reaction of the Third World is to question why they should control population growth if the West does not. Indeed on many occasions I have heard people in Kenya say, with some justification, 'It just looks as if you think there are too many of us.' I recently lectured on the Kora Research Project at a conference at the Commonwealth Institute in London and was astounded to hear a representative of an international body state that 'carrying capacity in relation to humans is just a metaphor'. If there was no observable effect of climate on food production, it might well be a metaphor, but since the relationship between climate and primary production (food availability) has been proved beyond all doubt, we may conclude that these resources are finite, and as such must be taken into account when considering human population problems.

The increase in population has already had a profound effect on the local environment in Kenya. Farming has been extended onto steep slopes and dangerously close to rivers, where tilling leads to massive soil erosion, while local modification of the vegetation has resulted in lowered fertility, and erosion by wind and water. During the period 1965–72, 6000 hectares (15,000 acres) of forest were converted annually to agriculture in Kenya, which has inevitably led to increased run-off and decreased productivity, as well as to an increased danger from fire in the dry season in the recently felled vegetation. Inevitably many effects are felt far from the site of the disturbance, and in particular the increased silt load now carried by the Tana as a result of present farming practices is causing major problems. Indeed, silt carried by the Tana had been filling the storage reservoirs to such an extent that a 1968 report on the further development of this resource stated: 'It is necessary to ensure that soil erosion in future does not exceed present levels on account of its adverse effect on the storage function of reservoirs.' The silt loss below Kamburu before the dam here was constructed was 270 million kg (594 million lb) per annum, which it was estimated would reduce the storage capacity by 15 per cent over the next fifty years, providing the conditions at the time prevailed.

Compared with other areas with similar characteristics, sediment figures in the middle Tana basin are very high. Oddly enough, the highland regions where intensive agriculture is practised have fairly low sediment yields, suggesting that the greatest damage is done in the more sensitive areas at lower altitudes into which the population has now moved. The increase in sediment load has had a profound influence on Kenya's rivers and the uses to which they are put, for it increases the cost of water treatment, impairs the efficiency of hydroelectric turbines, reduces fish populations in both inland and offshore waters, increases the quantity of fertilizers and pesticides carried by the river, and also increases the frequency with which rivers on flood plains shift their courses and overflow their banks. In the Kora National Reserve, far downstream from the Kamburu dam, the continuously changing water levels are affecting the sand-banks, and many elements of the local fauna.

Conservation has a meaning far beyond the preservation of a single animal and plant species, for the world is slowly beginning to realize that, if developing nations are to increase their standard of living, the conservation of natural resources must be seen to be a practical contribution to this important and perfectly understandable aim. Regrettably many conservation organizations still have a paternal attitude to conservation in the Third World, where their efforts are often viewed as a form of neocolonialism, with the comfortably-off telling the developing world what to do whilst they sip their pink gins. We should perhaps remember that the manner in which developed countries consume inordinate quantities of goods and luxuries which are derived from the natural resources of Third World countries means so often that much of the environmental damage that horrifies us today is in many respects our responsibility. If the perfectly laudable aims of conservation bodies are ever to have a really lasting impact, it is necessary for their plans to benefit the local human population, as well as the wildlife. *The World Conservation Strategy* published jointly by the International Union for the Conservation of Nature, UNEP and the World Wildlife Fund in 1980 departed from the narrower preservationist attitude and pointed out the urgent need not only to increase the amount of aid to developing countries, but also to allocate a greater proportion of that aid to ensuring that conservation was closely integrated with development.

The need for such an approach would seem self-evident when one sees agricultural plots established on steep slopes, or valuable forest destroyed for firewood or subsistence farming, yet the environmentally obvious is frequently not evident to those who plan development projects. Such a case has been highlighted by Francine Hughes' research project on the lower Tana River. She quickly realized that the establishment of the Bura Irrigation Settlement Project had created problems that had never been taken into consideration when it was first planned, namely that the influx of a large human population has had a damaging effect on the valuable and unique riverine forest as the local people have used it as a source of timber for construction and firewood. The very recent establishment of irrigated plantations to provide much-needed firewood has only partly alleviated the problem of forest destruction. Such difficulties are not uncommon, for ecologists are seldom involved at the planning stage of projects of this kind and little attention is usually given to monitoring the impact of the project once it has been completed. Francine Hughes observes that bodies as prestigious as the World Bank have only just begun to recognize the urgent need to integrate sound environmental management principles with their development programmes.

220

Agriculture has not had and is unlikely to have much impact on Kora, for the arid climate makes it unsuitable for even the crudest attempts at subsistence farming. This prediction was confirmed by the Landsat images which indicated that, although the area of farming land to the east had increased between 1976 and 1979, there was no further penetration downwards into Kora. The major danger lies in the increasing pressure from pastoralists who enter the Reserve from all directions in search of grazing for their cattle, and browse for their camels, sheep and goats. It has been estimated that the pastoral population of Kenya numbered some 1.5 million individuals in 1972, who maintained herds of 4.5 million cattle, 0.75 million camels, and 2.3 million sheep and goats. After the introduction of domestic-animal vaccination schemes in 1942, the herd population expanded dramatically until it was rapidly depleted by a severe drought in 1960, an example of a pattern that is now well known. The pastoral peoples themselves recognize a continuing cycle in which herd expansion is followed by range destruction and then herd decimation by drought, when famine relief is necessary – and then the cycle starts all over again. This pattern is also closely related to the degree of erosion in arid country, which is increased when the animal population is high. Vegetation will in due course reestablish itself once stock numbers fall, but only provided the damage is not too great. As stock are a form of wealth it has been suggested that pastoralists will always carry too many animals, but where tribes are living on a renewable protein resource such as blood and milk, the number of animals they need is a herd that will sustain them at the height of the dry season, not the rains, when they could bath in milk if they so desired. The well-known ornithologist and agriculturalist, the late Leslie Brown, carried out a profound study of the Masai, in which he examined the relationship between the number of animals maintained, and the number of people. His conclusion was that habitat and range damage was caused by too many people, rather than by too many animals, for the increasing human population demanded that the tribe kept larger herds to sustain themselves through all the seasons.

The recurrence of the drought conditions that we experienced in Kora, and which that part of the world continues to experience, is something that has been the subject of considerable investigation within the arid Sahel zone which lies just to the south of the great Sahara desert and which is said to be advancing southwards at an alarming rate. Although the spread of this zone is in part due to increasing numbers of pastoralists, who have overgrazed their pasture, and to the removal of forest to the south, it has been recently suggested that a primary factor in Sahelian advance in west Africa has been the eradication of the tsetse fly. Formerly this fly, which transmits the dreaded sleeping sickness (nagana) to cattle, prevented the movement of domestic stock into the Sahelian areas, but the eradication of the fly has accelerated pastoral penetration and the accompanying degradation of the range. Interestingly, fly-eradication programmes have been intended to assist development, but have in fact resulted in the drastic reduction of the carrying capacity of these regions.

Over the whole area of arid Africa, however, there is increasing evidence to

221

ORMEROD, E.M., Rev., 'Journey on the Tana River', *Geog. J.* 8 (1896), 283-90.

ORMEROD, W.E., 'The Relationship between Economic Development and Ecological Degradation: How Degradation has occurred in West Africa and how the Progress might be halted', *J. Arid. Envir.* 1 (1978), 357-79.

PATEL, R., EVANS, M., and MITCHELL, A., Mammal Survey, *Tana River Expedition Report*, 1976.

RAVENSTEIN, E.G., 'Journey to the Upper Tana, 1889', *Proc. Roy. Geog. Soc.* and monthly record of *Geog.* 3 (1890), 129-36.

PITTAWAY, T., and KIBUWA, S., Botany Survey, *Tana River Expedition Report*, 1976.

PRATT, D.J., GREENWAY, P.J., and GWYNNE, M.D., 'A Classification of East African Rangeland with an Appendix on Terminology', *J. App. Ecol.* 3 (1966), 369-82.

PRATT, D.J., and GWYNNE, M.D., *Rangeland Management and Ecology in East Africa* (Hodder and Stoughton, 1977).

ROSENGARTEN, F., *The Book of Spices* (Pyramid Books, New York, 1973).

ROSS, J.H., 'A Conspectus of the African Acacia Species', *Mem. Bot. Surv. S.Africa* 44 (1979).

ROSS, W.M., 'A Journey down the Tana River in East Africa', *United Empire* 4 (1913), 331-5.

RZOSKA, J., 'Observations on Tropical Rain Pools and General Remarks on Temporary Waters', *Hydrobiologia* 17 (1961), 265-86.

SALE, J., 'Kenya blend', *Punch*, 27 April, 1983, 41-2.

STILES, D., and MURO-HAY, S.C., 'Stone Cairn Burials at Kokurmatakore, Northern Kenya', *Azania* 16 (1981), 151-66.

STILES, D., 'The Azanian Civilisation and Megalithic Cushites Revisited', *Kenya Past and Present* 16 (1983), 20-7.

TYRELL, J.G., and COE, M.J., 'The Rainfall Regime of Tsavo National Park, Kenya, and its Phenological Significance', *J. Biogeog.* (1974), 187-92.

VERDCOURT, B., and TRUMP, E.C., *Common Poisonous Plants of East Africa* (Collins, 1969).

WHITEHEAD, P.J.D., 'Notes on a Collection of Fishes from the Tana River below Garissa, Kenya', *J.E. Afr. Nat. Hist. Soc.* 23 (4) (1959), 167-71.

WILLIAMS, J.G., *A Field Guide to the National Parks of East Africa* (Collins, 1967).

WILLIAMS, J.G., and ARLOTT, N., *A Field Guide to the Birds of East Africa* (Collins, 1980).

YOUNG, A., *Tropical Soils and Soil Survey* (Cambridge University Press, 1976).

Expedition Members

KENYA MEMBERS

Issa Aggundey *Small mammals*
Denny Anguin *Birds*
Dr Ken Campbell *Fish*
Michael Cheptumo *Reptiles*
Mike Clifton *Insects*
Dr Michael Gwynne *Satellite imagery*
Patrick Hamilton *Large mammals*
Dr Jim Hebrard *Reptiles*
Christine Kabuye *Plants*
Dr G. Key *Small mammals*
Richard Leakey *Co-leader*
Jon Loman *Reptiles*
Alex Mackay *Reptiles/scorpions*
Dr Tom Madson *Reptiles*
Joseph Muhangani *Insects*
Geoffrey Mungai *Plants*
Cecelia Muringo *Birds*
Joseph Mutanga *Plants*
John Njoroge *Insects*
Dr Steven Njuguna *Freshwater biologist*
Professor Celia Nyamwesu *Geomorphology*
Moses Olang *Weight of standing vegetation*
Fred Pertet *Large mammals*
Martin Pickford *Molluscs*
Dr Mark Ritchie *Insects*
Damaris Rotich *Reptiles*
Dr C. van Someren *Birds*
Dr Daniel Stiles *Anthropology*

UK/RGS MEMBERS

Dr Andrew Agnew *Plant community structure*
Dr Sky Alibhai *Small mammals*

Nicola Bennett-Jones *Project nurse*
Deborah Boys *Administrative assistant*
Christopher Coe *Fish*
Dr Malcolm Coe *Co-leader and rock outcrops*
Dr Mark Collins *Insects*
Sir Vivian Fuchs *President RGS*
Professor Andrew Goudie *Geomorphology*
Lord Hamish Hay *Administrative assistant*
Cpl. T. Hampson *Camp building*
Chris Hemming *Habitat survey*
Dr John Hemming *Director RGS*
Dr Brent Holben *NASA/GSFC – satellite ground truth*
Mark Hughes *Land Rover engineer*
Sgt. W.P. Inglis *Camp building*
Dr Bent Juel-Jensen *Medical officer*
Dr Chris Justice *NASA/GSFC – satellite ground truth*
Michael Keating *Administrative assistant*
Timothy Palmer *Camp building assistant*
Robin Payne *Plant studies assistant*
Dr K. Pye *Geomorphology*
Michael Saunders *Fish*
Victoria Southwell *Photographer*
Roy Vincent *Land Rover engineer*
Dr Peter G. Waterman *Phytochemistry of resins*
Andrew Watson *Geomorphology*
Dr Murray Watson *Habitat survey*
Chris West *Insects*
Nigel de N. Winser *Field director*

Sponsors

Ecological investigations rely heavily on funds and support from a wide variety of sources and the Kora Research Project is no exception.

The Royal Geographical Society, the National Museums of Kenya, the Ministry of Tourism and Wildlife (Wildlife Conservation and Management Department) and all 55 British and Kenyan members of the Project would like to acknowledge the considerable support and enthusiasm offered to this survey in cash and kind both before and after the field phases. It enabled a full baseline survey of the flora and fauna of the Kora National Reserve to be undertaken, which will contribute to the future development and conservation of the area.

Particular thanks go to the seven major sponsors of the project, without whose timely support the project could never have taken place:

Barclays Bank (Kenya) Ltd
British Airways
Ker and Downey Safaris (Kenya) Ltd
Land Rover Ltd
Otis Elevators (Kenya) Ltd
Overseas Development Administration
Royal Society

We are also indebted to the following bodies, companies and individuals for their invaluable association with the Project and for their vision in supporting this research. It is hoped that the project has been a catalyst to focus attention on this little known but important ecosystem on the Tana River, and that future researchers from Kenya and overseas will be able to build on the substantial baseline data collected during the course of the Kora Research Project 1983-4.

Abbott Laboratories Ltd
Achelis (Kenya) Ltd
George Adamson
Terence Adamson
African Medical and Research Foundation
African Wildlife Leadership Foundation
Alibhai Shariff and Sons (Kenya) Ltd
Alitalia (Kenya) Ltd
American Businessman's Club (Kenya)

Ames Division of Miles
Amini Charitable Trust
Jock Anderson
Astra Pharmaceuticals Ltd
Atlas Copco (Kenya) Ltd
Automobile Association of East Africa
Avis (Kenya) Ltd

Bacho Record Tools
Barclays Bank International

Peter Barry
Ian Barton
BAT (Kenya) Ltd
BATLSK
Bayer UK Ltd
BBC Radio 4
Beecham Products
Bencard
Mrs Ruth Bennett-Jones
Berk Pharmaceuticals Ltd
Bonar (EA) Ltd
Boots Company Ltd
Bridport Gundry Marine Ltd
Michael Bright (Radio 4)
Brillo
British Council
British Business Association (Kenya)
British High Commission, Kenya
British Land Company PLC
Brooke Bond Group PLC
Brooke Bond (Kenya) Ltd
Bulldog Leisurewear

Calmic UK Ltd
Caltex Oil (Kenya) Ltd
Camerapix
Camping Gaz
Chandaria Supplementary Foundation
Chequered Flag
Chloride Exide (Kenya) Ltd
Ciba Geigy (Kenya) Ltd
Coca Cola Corporation
W.H. Collier
Colmans UK Ltd
The Commonwealth Foundation
Comp-Rite (Kenya) Ltd
Cooper Motor Corporation (Kenya) Ltd
Coopers and Lybrand (Kenya) Ltd
Cow and Gate Ltd
Credit Finance Corporation (Kenya)
Sgt. Derek Cummock

Derek Dames
Davis and Shirtliff (Kenya) Ltd
Captain Alan Dennis
Desert Locust Control Organization for Eastern Africa
Direct Foods
Dista Products Ltd
Drinkmaster Ltd
Dudley Stationery
Duncan, Flockhart and Co Ltd
Dunlop (Kenya) Ltd
Durham University Exploration Society

East African Industries (Kenya) Ltd

East African Packing Industries (Kenya) Ltd
East African Wildlife Safaris (Kenya) Ltd
East African Wildlife Society
D.J. Edelman Ltd
Elephence (Kenya) Ltd
Endebess Estates (Kenya) Ltd
Esso Standard (Kenya) Ltd
Sandy Evans

James Finlay (Kenya) PLC
Firestone East Africa (Kenya) Ltd
Fisons Pharmaceuticals Ltd
Tony Fitzjohn
Mr and Mrs Dick Flatt
Flying Doctors' Society of Africa
Food Specialities (Kenya) Ltd

Geigy Pharmaceuticals
W.E. Gelson
The Geographical Magazine
Sir Alexander Gibb (Africa)
Glaxo Laboratories Ltd
Dr E.D. Gordon
George Greenfield
The Grocers Company
Arthur Guinness Son and Co

Viscount Hambledon
Harrisons and Crosfield
Major Brian Hart, RAMC
Andrew Hartley
Dr John Hemming
Heritage Insurance Company (Kenya)
Hertfordshire Display Co Ltd
Hoffman La Roche and Co (Kenya) Ltd
Hogg Robinson (Kenya) Ltd
Holman Brothers (EA) Ltd
Homa Lime Company (Kenya)
Hough Hoseason and Co Ltd
House of Manji (Kenya) Ltd
Dr Francine Hughes

ICI Ltd
Inamdar and Co (Kenya) Ltd
International Aeradio EA Ltd

Janssen Pharmaceuticals Ltd
D. Jason
Jen Shoes
Messrs S.H. Johnson and Co Ltd
Johnson and Johnson Ltd

Karrimor International Ltd
Keith Johnson Photographic
Kenya Breweries (Kenya) Ltd
Kenya Canners Ltd
Kenya High Commission, London

234

Kenya Museum Society
Kenya News Agency
Kenya Orchards
Kenya Rangeland Ecological Monitoring
    Unit
Kenya Swiss Chemical Co
Kenya Wine Agencies
Ker/Downey/Block Memorial Fund
HE Bethuel Abdu Kiplagat
Kirby Laing Foundation
Ernest Kleinwort Charitable Trust
KLM (Kenya) Ltd
Kodak (Kenya) Ltd
Kora Preservation Wildlife Trust

Lacrinoid Products Ltd
Laughton and Sons
Mr and Mrs Leckie (Kenya)
Lederle Laboratories
Lewa Downs (Kenya) Ltd
Lion of Kenya Insurance Company (Kenya)
Lloyds Bank
London Fancy Box Co Ltd

Sir M. MacDonald and Partners
Machinery Services (Kenya)
Anthony Marion
Marine Electrics Ltd
Chris Marshall
Mercers Company
Dr Andreas Meyerhold
Metal Box Company (Kenya)
Mr and Mrs John Millard
Ms Pippa Millard
Ministry of Defence
Mitchell Cotts
Mobil Oil (Kenya) Ltd
Mowlem International Ltd
Motorola Sales and Services
Murphy Chemicals (EA) Ltd
Muthaiga Club

Nabisco Ltd
Nairobi Hospital
Napp Laboratories Ltd
National Industrial Credit (EA) Ltd
NERC
Nicholas Laboratories Ltd
Nikon Ltd

Observer Magazine
Ogilvy and Mather (EA) Ltd
Order of St John
Ove Arup and Partners
Oxford Town and Gown Scholarship

Parke Davis and Co Ltd

Penguin Books
Pfizer Ltd
Pharmax Ltd
George Philip and Son Ltd
Philip Harris (Holdings) PLC
Phoenix East Africa Assurance Co
Poulton Fund
John Porter, RE
Print Associates (Kenya)
Prudential Assurance Co (Kenya) Ltd

Reckitt and Colman (Kenya) Ltd
Reckitt and Colman Ltd
Richardsons of Leicester Ltd
Rio Tinto Zinc
Roche Products Ltd
N.M. Rothschild and Sons Ltd
Roussel Laboratories Ltd
Royal Air Force
Royal Botanic Gardens, Kew
Royal Entomological Society of London
Royal Insurance Co (Kenya) Ltd
Ryvita Co Ltd

Sabatani Taylor Associates
St Ivel Ltd
Sandoz Products Ltd
Mr and Mrs C.R. Saunders
Schwartz Spices
Scout Shops
Searle Pharmaceuticals
Sedgwick International Ltd
Seton Products Ltd
John Sidders, RE
Smith and Nephew Pharmaceuticals
Smith Kline and French Laboratories
    Ltd
Socfinaf Co (Kenya) Ltd
Miss Victoria Southwell
Professor Sir Richard Southwood
Squibb E.R. and Sons Ltd
Stafford-Miller Ltd
Stanley Tools
Steadman and Associates (Kenya)
J. and W. Stuart Ltd
Sunbird Aviation (Kenya) Ltd
Supreme Plastics Ltd

Sheikh A. Taib and Sons (Mwingi) Ltd
Tate and Lyle
Television International Enterprises Ltd
Thermos Ltd
J. Walter Thompson Co Ltd
Thor Hammers
3M Company
Mr and Mrs Peter Tilbury

Timsales Ltd
Total Oil Products (EA) Ltd
Travenol Laboratories Ltd
Tropical Car Hire
Twiga Chemical Industries Ltd

Unilever PLC
University of Oxford – Lockey Bequest
John Ure
United Nations Environment Programme (Global Environment Monitoring System)

Vernon-Carus Ltd
Victor Laurence (Merchants) Ltd
Vitafoam (Kenya) Ltd

Warner Lambert Central Africa
Warner Lambert UK Ltd
Warner, William R. and Co Ltd
WB Pharmaceuticals Ltd
Weetabix Ltd
Wellcome Medical Division
Whitecap Safaris
Wiggins Teape (Kenya) Ltd
George Williamson (Kenya) Ltd
Windmill Brush Company
Winthrop Laboratories
Wolfson College
Wrights of London
Wyeth Laboratories

Index